£12·95

# Ores and Minerals
## Introducing Economic Geology

# Ores and Minerals
## *introducing economic geology*

**J. W. Barnes**
*Department of Earth Sciences*
*University College of Swansea*

OPEN UNIVERSITY PRESS
Milton Keynes • Philadelphia

Open University Press
Open University Educational Enterprises Limited
12 Cofferidge Close
Stony Stratford
Milton Keynes MK11 1BY, England

*and*
242 Cherry Street
Philadelphia, PA 19106, USA

First Published 1988

**British Library Cataloguing in Publication Data**

Barnes, John W.
  Ores and minerals: an introduction to the economic aspects of geology.
  1. Geology, Economic
  I. Title
  553     TN260

  ISBN 0–335–15216–3

  ISBN 0–335–15213–9 Pbk

Project management: Clarke Williams

Printed in Great Britain by
Thomson Litho Ltd, East Kilbride, Scotland

# Contents

# Preface

No graduate who has studied any geology should leave university without at least some knowledge of how it is applied to the mineral industry. This book is designed to fill that need. It is meant not only for students who take geology merely as a first-year subsidiary subject but also for those who study it as a principal subject but have not opted for courses in applied geology. Teachers of A-level geology may also find it a useful guide. Readers are assumed to have already completed most of their first-year geology course, and also to have some knowledge of elementary chemistry. The object is not to dig deeply into economic geology, but to indicate its scope and its influence on many aspects of our lives.

The subject is introduced by an outline of the present mineral industry and its historical development. Ore minerals are described, with an account of how minerals are altered during erosion, to the extent that many of them are no longer easily recognizable at surface. The ways in which ores are formed are then explained, one chapter covering those deposited during sedimentation, one for those closely related to volcanic activity, and one for ores associated with intrusive rocks. Emphasis is on the great diversity of ore genesis and, as this obviously affects the way in which we look for new ore fields, a chapter on prospecting is included. Geological sources of energy are considered next, such as the natural fossil fuels (coal, oil and gas), the synfuels processed from oil shales and tar sands, and the several forms of geothermal energy. The industrial, i.e. the non-metallic, minerals are also covered, for their total annual value in a developed country exceeds that of the metallic minerals. Another chapter is reserved for the most important of all minerals — water. Finally, the role of the geologist in all the various stages of mineral exploration and exploitation is described.

It is hoped that this book will round off the geological education of those whose acquaintance with the subject has been limited to a one-year course, by demonstrating that geology is more than a purely academic subject. For those geologists who interests are purely academic, this book may expand their outlook, or even stimulate their interest in the more economic aspects of their science. Abundant references to other works are made for those who wish to take a deeper interest in economic geology.

# Acknowledgements

Many have contributed to the production of this book. Among those who deserve a special mention are Vivian Jenkins and Wendy Johnston who typed the script, and Stephen Hibbs for his photographic expertise. Criticism and help on certain chapters was also given by Peter Styles and Geraint Owen. All are members of the Department of Earth Sciences of University College of Swansea. I also wish to thank Dr Tony Evans of the University of Leicester, for reading the manuscript and making many useful suggestions. A special thanks is offered to my family: to my wife, Mary, who read drafts, corrected spelling, and read proofs; to Richard and Karen, who did the bulk of the indexing; and to Duncan for the photo in Fig. 7.7.

Acknowledgement is also made to the following, who have given their permission to reproduce illustrations which form the following diagrams:

Figure 4.3 from A.M. Evans (1980). *An Introduction to Ore Geology*, Edinburgh, Blackwell Scientific Publication, pp. 138–9.

Figure 4.4 from H. Colley (1976). Classification and exploration guide for Kuroko-type deposits based on occurrences in Fiji. *Trans. Inst. Min. Metall.* **85**, p. B195.

Figures 7.12 and 7.16 from *The Earth's Physical Resources* — Block 2 (1973). *Energy resources*, Milton Keynes, Open University. Based on BGS material by permission of the Director, British Geological Survey: Crown Copyright Reserved.

Figures 7.13, 7.14 and 7.15 from G.C. Brown and E. Skipsey (1986). *Energy Resources*, Milton Keynes, Open University Press, pp. 25, 28 and 29.

*Department of Earth Sciences*
*University College of Swansea*
*July, 1987*

# CHAPTER 1

# Mines and the mineral industry

## 1.1 The birth of mining

### 1.1.1 Flints and pigments

Agriculture and mining are the basic raw material industries. Of the two, mining is the oldest. It started some 300,000 years ago with the search for tool-making materials whilst man was still a hunter. This was the Palaeolithic or Old Stone Age when stone, bone, and wood were all that was available; bone and wood were at hand, stone was needed to obtain them. Some stones were better than others for tool making. Flint and obsidian could be chipped and ground to sharp cutting edges, so could quartzite, although less easily. That some regions were better endowed than others led to the earliest trading routes, as factory districts became established. Large-scale flint mining began in Britain well before 3000 BC. Grimes Graves in Norfolk was one important district; there, ancient underground workings occur over a wide area and many can still be entered.

Stone tools served man until the end of the Neolithic or New Stone Age, and well beyond it. Agriculture had by then replaced hunting as the main source of food, and people had settled into villages. But not only stone was dug from the ground during the Stone Ages; pigments were mined as well, both for painting cave walls and for body decoration. Natural iron oxides (ochres), and iron-rich clays (umbers), were probably the first to be used; one extensive underground working found in Swaziland has been carbon-dated at 40,000 years BC.

Other mineral pigments were also known. Cinnabar, the bright red mercury sulphide, was mined in central Turkey 8000 years ago for vermilion. Wad, a manganese oxide, was used for black; the lead sulphide, galena, gave grey and was also used by the ancient Egyptians as eye-shadow. Later stibnite, antimony sulphide, provided the black cosmetic stibio (or *kohl*) with which Jezebel 'painted her face', or so St Jerome's Bible says. Perhaps attempts to purify such pigments led to the discovery of smelting, for Neolithic beads of smelted lead have been found in Turkey pre-dating any other smelting known by over two thousand years.

### 1.1.2 The first metals

Copper was the first metal to be used, dating back well into the Neolithic of Turkey, Iran, and Iraq. It was discovered because it can occur 'native', that is as a natural metal in nature. Few other metals occur this way; gold nearly always does, silver and platinum sometimes do, mercury occasionally does. With rare exceptions all other metals can survive in nature only as chemical compounds. Of all the native metals, copper is by far the most abundant, and is often found in large and jagged pieces. Neolithic man probably first found it in the same way we find broken glass on the beach — by cutting his feet on it when fording streams. One source of native copper was in eastern Turkey where copper needles and scrapers 9000 years old have been found 20 km downstream from the present Ergani Maden copper mine on the Tigris.

Native copper was first treated as a rather ductile stone; it was hammered and ground to shape. But hammering made it brittle through work-hardening, a property common to all metals. Smiths soon found copper could be softened again by heating it and allowing it to cool slowly; they had discovered annealing. There is a temptation to assume that this pre-heating eventually led to melting and casting, but it is unlikely that an ordinary fire would have been hot enough. Copper may even have been smelted from its ores before it was found possible to melt it. Early copper-smelting centres were closely associated with coloured pottery industries, and it has been suggested that pieces of the blue and green copper carbonate minerals used as pigments were left in the kilns and later found to be reduced to sponge copper, very like native copper in appearance. Pottery kilns of the time were certainly hot enough for this, and pots were fired in the same type of reducing atmosphere needed to produce metal from ore. The school-book explanation, that smelting was discovered when stones containing copper ore were reduced to metal when inadvertently used to support cooking pots, is most improbable. Such conditions would have been oxidizing, and a domestic fire unlikely to provide enough heat even in a howling gale. Really, we do not know how smelting was discovered and it may always remain an intriguing mystery.

### 1.1.3 Alloys and bronze

Once smelting had been discovered, probably in the mountains of eastern Turkey or the Caucasus in about 4500–4000 BC experiment or chance brought arsenical copper ores to the smelter; arsenical copper alloys resulted. These melted at a lower temperature than copper, they did not absorb oxygen and so were easier to cast without cavities, and they gave a harder and stronger product which took a better edge. By about 3000 BC tin began to replace arsenic in alloys and the true Bronze Age had arrived, at least it had in the Middle East, for Europe lagged far behind. Where did the tin come from? Although it must have come from somewhere in the area, sites are yet to be positively identified. Little tin was needed and the deposits were probably very small; two tonnes a year was probably enough for the whole Ancient world. Later, tin was mined near Samarkand, and ancient tin workings have recently been found in the Eastern Egyptian Desert, but apparently not old enough to account for Early Bronze Age use. Tin was exported from Saxony, Iberia, and eventually Britain. But Britain was not the Kassiterides, the Tin Islands of the Greeks; that honour goes to the trading posts established on the islands of the Loire Estuary in France, although the tin traded there was probably largely British.

### 1.1.4 The 'seven metals of Antiquity'

Other metals followed the discovery of copper. Gold was known from about 4000 BC, as was silver. Both were mined as native metal, and the legend of Jason's search for the Golden Fleece is almost certainly based on a factual Bronze Age gold rush to the eastern Black Sea, where alluvial gold was collected on sheep skins, a method used in primitive mining even today. It was soon found that silver could be extracted from lead ore, and lead is still the main source of silver: silver is principally a by-product metal. Lead itself seems to have had little appeal until about 1200 BC, probably because it is a soft and unattractive metal. Its use grew with the development of plumbing and pewter.

The most important discovery was that of iron. At first iron was a by-product from copper smelting, accidentally produced when furnaces overheated; rare iron artefacts have been found dating from 2800 BC. Limonite, an iron oxide mineral, was a common flux used in ancient smelting. Overheating reduced it to iron droplets which percolated down to accumulate as a 'bear' below the furnace floor. This sponge-like iron could be recovered at intervals and wrought to shape. As it occurred only rarely, and then by chance, it was expensive, and Assyrian records of 1950 BC show that iron was worth five times its weight in gold; only kings could afford it. By 1300 BC the Hittites had discovered how to produce iron purposely; they tyred their chariots with it to give them greater mobility in battle. By 500 BC iron had spread to Britain in the west and China in the east.

By the start of the Christian era all 'seven metals of Antiquity' were known, namely copper, tin, gold, silver, lead, iron, and mercury. Manganese was present in many famous irons, such as those from the Chalybes, but it was part of the ore and so unrecognized. Zinc and arsenic were used in copper alloys but they were either a natural part of the ore or were added to alloys as compounds which did not look metallic. Even tin was probably first unknowingly added to copper as the oxide mineral cassiterite, or tinstone, to make bronze. As far as the ancients were concerned, bronze was a distinct metal, harder than copper and a different colour. When they added the white zinc carbonate mineral smithsonite to copper, another new metal — brass — resulted, more gold-like than copper. Is it to be wondered if they concluded that they had only to find the right stone to make gold? Almost certainly early alloying gave birth to the search for the philosopher's stone.

Other metallic mineral compounds were used only as pigments, such as the black of fine-ground stibnite, the orange-red and yellow of the arsenical sulphides, realgar and orpiment. Cobalt and nickel minerals were used to colour ceramics, enamels, and glasses. These metals and metalloids were, with some very minor additions, all that were needed until the Industrial Revolution of the eighteenth century.

### 1.1.5  The Industrial Revolution

As the interest in chemistry promoted by the Industrial Revolution led to the discovery of more metals, uses were found for them. Despite this, there was little pressure or need to search for new sources of metallic ores. The supply was adequate, with chance finds topping up the mineral inventory.

It was the chance find of Californian gold in 1849 that sparked off a world-wide interest in prospecting. California could not accommodate all those who flocked to her goldfields, so many moved elsewhere. They found gold in Colorado and Nevada; some found it in eastern and western Australia, others went to Africa and found it in the Witwatersrand and in what is now Zimbabwe; gold was found in the Klondike, in Alaska and in the islands of the western Pacific. During the search for gold, other metals were found. Copper was discovered in Western USA in quantities far larger than in Europe, and in Australia. At first the ore was sent to Britain to be smelted with the domestic ores from Devon, Cornwall and Ireland, but smelters were soon built close to the mines, under-cutting European metal prices and ruining the British mines and smelters. Then huge amounts of cheaply-worked tin ore were found in south-east Asia, swamping the European tin industry, including Cornwall. Potential supplies of metals increased all over the world.

As the metal industry moved into the 20th century, the search for metals grew as industry grew, but the search was mainly by engineers with only a limited, if practical, knowledge of geology. As the century progressed, however, more and more geologists were enlisted to prospect for metals. They have been so successful that they have converted a pending copper shortage into a potential glut.

### 1.1.6  Fuels

Coal was used as a domestic fuel in Europe for centuries, although seldom far from its source owing to distribution difficulties. Some was traded in coastal vessels as 'sea coal' and, even as long ago as 1273, London banned it use owing to the smog it caused. In 1709 Abraham Darby first produced coke as a substitute for charcoal in smelting iron ores. The cost of iron fell, iron products became more affordable and new industries developed around coalfields where cheap fuel lay. Thus the Industrial Revolution began. Coal was wanted; it was the only industrial fuel. By 1800 Britain was producing 10 million tonnes a year; by 1900 the figure was 225 million (Foley 1976). Today, Britain produces little over 100 million tonnes against a world total of 3000 million, but now there are other sources of energy, including oil.

Engineers dominated the coal industry to almost the middle of this century. Coal sources which had been known for centuries were exploited to greater depths and on larger scales. In many countries coal could be mined cheaply from open pits. Even in the well-developed fields of Britain in the 1930s routine geological work was left to the mine surveyor. Since then, geologists have shown they can trace faulted seams and delineate coalfields better, and can also find concealed coalfields whose presence had hitherto been unknown; those of Oxfordshire and north-east Leicestershire are but two examples. In Europe and the United States we tend to think of coal as a Carboniferous mineral, after all, that is how the system got its name, but not all coals are Carboniferous. A few are older, many are younger. Nor are all coals hard coals; in many parts of the world, brown coals and lignites are the main solid fossil fuels.

Those other fossil fuels, oil and gas, are looked upon as modern fuels but, in fact, both have been known longer than coal. The sacred fires of Baku on the shores of the Caspian inspired the Zoroastrian religion and, like the fires of the oracles, were really gas seeps set alight by natural causes. Asphalt, left by the evaporation of seeping oil, was the mortar which bound the bricks of the walls of ancient Jericho; the ancient Egyptians used it too, to mummify their dead; and it has caulked boats since man first ventured upon water. The Romans collected liquid oil for their lamps from seeps, but it was the Chinese, in 200 BC, who drilled the first oil well, although by chance, for they were drilling for brine. Despite these minor uses, oil as an industry is traditionally dated from 1859, the year that Colonel Drake (the title was self-assumed) struck oil at 69 feet in Oil Creek, Pennslyvania. Nearly two hundred more wells were drilled during the following year. By 1900, world oil production had reached almost 20 million tonnes a year; in 1982 the figure was 2720 million.

The natural gas industry is even younger, for gas could not become a common fuel until it could be widely distributed. This became possible with the manufacture of cheap seamless steel piping in the 1930s. Now gas is piped over great distances, often along the sea floor: it can also be liquefied and transported in ships as LNG and LPG (liquid natural gas and liquid petroleum gas).

Despite considerable wildcat exploration (i.e. entrepreneurial drilling based on guesswork, fragmentary knowledge, hunches, or just plain hope) the oil industry was quick to see the need for geologists to exploit known fields and to find new ones. Because geologists themselves needed help to look for structures deep beneath the surface, the science of applied geophysics also developed. Today, oil exploration and exploitation is based firmly on geology and geophysics, aided by a wide range of electronic instrumentation, including the electronic logging of wells as they are drilled.

The last decade has seen a growing interest in tapping the earth's own natural heat. Geothermal energy is not a new idea; the Romans built baths around hot springs. On much larger scales, the Italians began to tap thermal springs for energy early in this century; New Zealand, Iceland, and many other countries followed suit. In all these cases, natural hot water, superheated water or steam have been used. Now research is being done to extract natural heat from the rocks themselves by pumping water deep into areas of high thermal gradient and retrieving it at elevated temperatures.

Uranium is the most modern of all fuels. Because it is radioactive, it is fairly easy to find, but in its radioactivity also lies its problems. The search for it's ores is a geological-cum-geophysical process, with few complications; the difficulties arise in the disposal of the radioactive industrial wastes after it has been used. Geologists have been asked to find safe places to store them underground, where they cannot contaminate the environment or leak into natural waters which might find their way to the surface. In this book we are concerned basically with the occurrence of mineral commodities; thankfully, we will leave the problems of their disposal to others.

### 1.1.7 Industrial minerals

The industrial mineral industry is the oldest industry of all, as the earliest tools were made of stone. Pigments were also in very early use, as were salt and edible phosphatic earths. Clay bricks date to Neolithic times, shaped building stone to the Bronze Age. Non-metallic minerals have been in continual use ever since, and now the non-metallics exceed the metallics in value by over 25 per cent in the economies of developed countries. They are used in all branches of industry; they provide constructional materials, chemicals, fluxes, fillers, fertilizers, abrasives, ceramics, cements and plasters. In the past, sources were well-known to the people who needed them; now, known resources in developed countries have been depleted and needs are often for very specific types of material. Again geologists are asked to show the way. But of all industrial materials, water is perhapes the most important. It is needed for industry, and for all domestic supplies right down to village level in less-developed countries, where piped supplies are unknown. Here geologists have proved themselves to be better water diviners than those who use more esoteric methods.

## 1.2  Ores, ore reserves and resources

### 1.2.1 Ore

Ore is best defined as a naturally-occurring mineral aggregate from which one or more useful constituents can be extracted. Extraction does not need to be profitable, for ores may be worked under subsidy or cost-plus agreements if a government wishes to encourage unprofitable mining; many do. By general consent, ores are considered, with a few exceptions, to be sources of metallic minerals. Industrial mineral bodies are not usually called ore.

An ore is merely a rather rare rock type. It consists of one or more valuable metallic minerals mixed with worthless gangue. The gangue may be rock, sedimentary, metamorphic, or igneous; it may be vein material, such as quartz, calcite, barite, and fluorite; often, it is unsaleable pyrite. Pyrite, however, is not always unsaleable; it may contain either cobalt or gold, and it is a useful source of by-product sulphur in the form of sulphuric acid. Unfortunately, in many regions by-product sulphuric acid is unsaleable, either because it is too far from a market, or because of over-supply in districts with large numbers of mines or with refineries of sulphur-rich oils.

The grade, i.e. metal content, of an ore varies from deposit to deposit. Whether an ore can be mined is a question of costs and metal prices; both vary. Cost of mining depends to a large extent on the geology of the ore body and its mineralogy, for these largely determine the mining method. Metal price is a function of world conditions and the rarity of the metal or ore. Good gold ores may contain less than 5 g/tonne or 5 parts per million (ppm) of gold (one sixth of an ounce per tonne). Some alluvial gold mines are worked by dredging down to under 0.5 g/tonne; at 1987 prices, 0.5 g of gold is worth over £4. Copper ores cannot be worked at such low grades. At around £1000/tonne of copper metal, about 0.6 per cent is the cut-off grade in huge open pit operations. Underground mines require better ore; a few may even reach 6 per cent copper, but average grades are from 2–4 per cent. Often by-products, such as cobalt or silver, effectively increase the value of the ore and allow lower copper grades to be worked. Some ores, such as those of chromium and aluminium, can only be worked when there is effectively no gangue present. Iron ores vary between about 30 and 70 per cent iron, with many averaging 45–50 per cent. Low grade iron ores can often be tolerated if they contain limestone gangue, for limestone must be added to smelt the ore; these ores are called self-fluxing.

### 1.2.2 Concentrates

Aluminium ores are smelted with little further treatment. Many iron and the more friable chrome ores are pelletized (moulded to marble-sized pellets) for more efficient smelting. Other ores are beneficiated or concentrated after mining. Concentration entails the removal of gangue minerals and, if an ore contains more than one metallic constituent, their minerals must be separated from each other too. The gangue minerals removed during concentration are called tailings; they go to waste. With very low grade ores, such as those in porphyry copper deposits, 99 per cent of the ore is gangue, and tailings disposal becomes a major problem. In some mines the wet fine-grained tailings from the concentration plant can be pumped back underground to support space left by mining.

Methods of beneficiation depend upon the mineralogical content of the ore. Heavy, abrasion-resistant minerals, such as gold and tinstone, can be separated from their gangue by taking advantage of their differences in specific gravity. Most base metal ore minerals, however, are soft, friable sulphides and are unsuitable for gravity separation. They are concentrated by froth flotation a method which depends on their surface chemistry, namely their differences in wettability. Some minerals are magnetic, or can be made magnetic by roasting, and magnetic separation is frequently a part of the beneficiation process. A few metals can be leached out of the ore: uranium is extracted this way, and much gold is leached from its ore by cyanide solutions.

### 1.2.3 Smelting and refining

Smelting and refining are not subjects to be covered in this book, except to say that both processes require fluxes and other mineral materials, including fuels, to sustain them. These must be found. Limestone and dolomite for iron smelting are usually in adequate supply; fluorite (fluorspar) for steel making is not, and is now more difficult to find than the iron ore itself. Graphite or zirconia is also needed to make crucibles for many metallurgical processes. Borax is a flux used in refining some metals. The supply of these materials is part of the industrial minerals industry and is as important in producing metals as the ores themselves.

### 1.2.4 Ore reserves and mineral resources

The main distinction between reserves and resources is that reserves are what you know you have, resources are what you hope you have. Reserves have been physically measured, resources are inferred. Reserves reflect the amount of ore present in a mine and are classified as proved, probable, and possible. Proved ore has been closely sampled in underground workings or by drilling, and there is a better than 90 per cent certainty that it exists in the tonnage and grade calculated. Probable ore is only a little less certain. Possible ore rests on less complete knowledge, including geological inference based on some physical evidence, and a knowledge of how the ore is known to occur. Measured, indicated, and inferred reserves are almost synonymous terms used by the United States Geological Survey.

Mineral resources include not only mineable ores but also all those deposits which are too low grade, or too difficult, to mine under present conditions. Rise in metal prices or improvements in technology may well make some unworkable ores economic. Resources also include deposits which have yet to be properly investigated, and those whose existence is assumed largely on geological possibility and probability. Resources may attract prospectors to a region in the hope that they may discover sizeable ore bodies. Economic geographers use the term mineral resources; so do politicians and journalists, usually with less justification or knowledge of what the words really mean.

## 1.3 Mining

Mines are places where minerals are extracted from the ground, either from open pits or underground workings. The word quarry is used where bulk minerals, such as limestone, are mined. The distinction is too subtle to worry about here, but it does have legal connotations.

Mines have to be found. The process starts with prospecting, or 'mineral exploration', which means much the same thing but sounds more scientific. When a promising prospect has been found it is pitted, trenched, and drilled to determine the shape of the ore body and to obtain samples for assay (analysis). Calculations can then be made of how much ore there is, its quality or grade, if it is worth mining, and how it can be mined. If the indications are favourable, and money can be raised, the next stage is development. Shafts are sunk or adits driven into the hillside if the mine is to be developed underground. Tunnels are driven to and through the ore (cross-cuts), and alongside the ore or in it (drifts), and the ore is eventually extracted in working places called stopes (see Fig. 1.1). Many shafts are sub-vertical and these days, because underground mines are tending more and more to use rubber-tyred equipment, some shafts are now gentle spiral declines and ore is hauled out in diesel trucks or lorries.

Open pits can be developed where ore bodies are large and the attitude of the ore permits it. Inevitably a stage is reached where waste (i.e. unproductive country rock) has to be mined to maintain stable pit walls (Fig. 1.2). At some stage the ratio of waste to ore becomes too high for profitable working; this is often about 2:1 (Fig. 1.3). Then the mine must be abandoned, or developed into a more expensively worked underground mine. This happened, for instance, at the former giant iron mine at Kiruna in arctic Sweden. Many smaller mines, however, start as a small, cheaply-worked open pit and, because some ores are

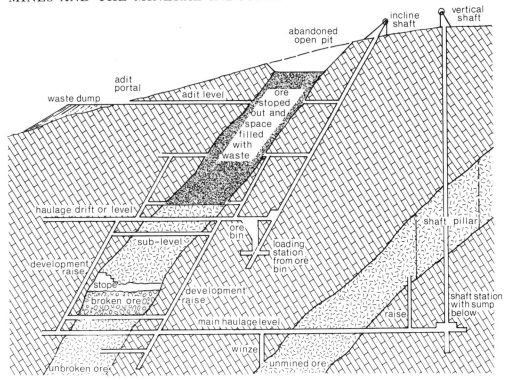

**Figure 1.1** Mining terminology. Ore was first mined from the outcrop as an open pit. An adit was driven into the hillside to cross-cut the ore at a deeper level. An incline shaft was sunk later to mine still deeper and, eventually, a vertical shaft was sunk to serve two ore bodies more efficiently. Ore is mined by driving two haulage drifts at different levels and connecting them by raises which are then connected by *sub-levels*. Ore is mined upwards from the lower sub-level to form a stope. Broken ore can be left in the stope to form a working platform and to support its walls (shrinkage stope), or withdrawn, and waste from the mill pumped in (cut-and-fill stoping). Ore between haulage and sub-level is left as supporting pillars until the level is abandoned. A shaft pillar is also left unmined.

enriched by weathering near to the surface, this may be a welcome bonus to the miner just when money is needed for development.

## 1.4  Importance of the mining industry

The importance of a domestic mining industry to a country cannot be overemphasized. This applies not only to metallic ores but to fuels and industrial minerals. The last named are particularly important for, although a country can import metals or even ores, it cannot afford to import many of the more bulky, low-value industrial minerals. On the other hand, metallic ores are an asset even to those countries which cannot use them themselves. Ores, concentrates, or smelted metals can be exported to earn foreign exchange with which to buy materials for

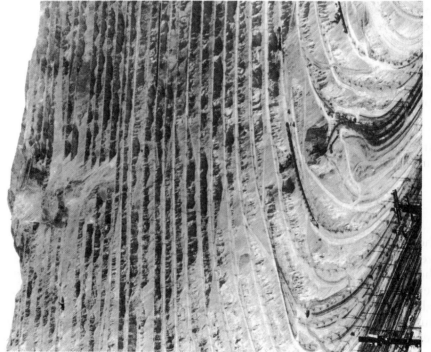

**Figure 1.2** *Left* Bingham open pit copper mine, Utah, USA. The pit is nearly a kilometre deep and has over 150 km of standard gauge railway tracks. Such pits are worked on a massive scale; *Right* a 175-tonne truck used at Butte in Montana, USA.

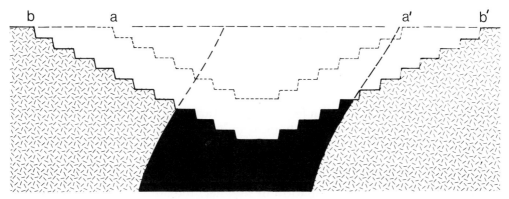

**Figure 1.3** Development of an open pit. During the early stages (a–a'), more ore is removed than waste rock; as the pit becomes deeper, the ratio of waste to ore mined becomes greater until at stage b–b' it is about 1.6:1. At Bingham, the limiting waste-to-ore ratio is about 2:1.

development. Some Third World governments have maintained that there is no need to exploit their ores until they are more fully developed. This can be a false economy, for many metals or ores go out of favour, or improvements in technology or new discoveries favour sources elsewhere. Beryl is an example: in the 1950s beryl was the main source of beryllium, and was mined from pegmatites mostly in the Third World. Since, then, huge deposits of beryllium have been found in bertrandite-bearing nodules which can be cheaply screened out of volcanic ashes in the western United States. The beryl-pegmatite market lost ground. Mercury is an example of a metal which has suffered lost markets, in this case over concern for environmental pollution. Many major mercury mines have now closed.

Of the metallic ores, iron is the most important to have. Many countries which once imported their steel now produce their own. Their economies have benefited from the work provided by the mines, the smelters, the fabricators, and the railways, not to mention the saving in foreign exchange. Some countries also benefit by having metals that other, more developed countries, almost wholly lack. Tin is one example; south-east Asia, South America, Australia, and Africa control 80 per cent of the world's supply. Gold is another, for the Republic of South Africa produces 68 per cent of the non-communist world's output. Little need be said of oil where so much centres around the Persian Gulf to the advantage of the adjoining states. By raising their prices far above the cost of production, OPEC (Organization of Petroleum Exporting Countries) affected the economies of many Third World countries adversely in addition to those of the more resilient developed nations. However, high oil prices could well kill off the goose that lays the oil producers' golden eggs for, until the large price fall in 1985, synfuels (oils extracted from shales, tar sands, and torbanites) were approaching a competitive production cost. Synfuel reserves are at least equal to those of liquid oil and lie almost exclusively outside OPEC territories.

Coal, the other major mineral fuel, has huge reserves which have yet to be exploited. Britain is particularly fortunate, for her coal should last for another 300 years. Coal is a versatile mineral and, like petroleum, can produce a wide range of by-products for the chemical industry. It can even yield petroleum at near-competitive costs when required, as South Africa has clearly demonstrated.

## 1.5 Conclusions

The mineral industry has had a long history, starting with the search for useful stones over 300,000 years ago. Without it, industrialization is impossible. Only a few hundred years ago the 'seven metals of antiquity' sufficed most of our metallic needs: industrial minerals were a little more varied, and used mainly for building and ceramics; mineral oils and coal were little used. Now, almost every element in the periodic table is used in one form or another, including many of those with almost unpronounceable names listed under the Rare Earths. We produce energy from coal, oil and uranium, and are now attempting to exploit the natural heat of the earth itself. To enable us to do all these things with minerals, and to find new sources, requires a knowledge of how mineral deposits were formed, why they were formed, and the specific types of geological environment in which each was formed. The purpose of this book is to indicate the type of geological knowledge needed to guide our exploitation of mineral deposits, and to find new ones.

# CHAPTER 2

# Ores and ore minerals

Ores are variable materials. Even within a single ore body there may be great differences in mineral composition and grade. A body may even change from copper ore to tin ore with increasing depth, as at Dolcoath in Cornwall. In addition, close to the surface, sulphide minerals oxidize, altering the whole character of the ore and its grade. Changes influence both mining and marketing, and may so radically affect beneficiation that plant needs modification or redesign to accommodate them. It is the task of the geologist to predict changes well in advance so that engineering staff can plan how to mine the ore, and how to treat it during different stages in the life of the mine. At least one mine has had to close down to rebuild its plant soon after opening because mineralogically the ore was not what was expected. Therefore, before we can study processes of ore formation, we need to know something about the minerals that compose the ore, their properties, and how they may alter.

## 2.1 Metal associations and by-products

Ore consists of ore minerals and gangue. A few ores, such as those of gold and tin, may often contain only one worthwhile ore mineral; others, notably of copper, may contain just one recoverable metal although it may be present in several different mineral forms. Most ores, however, contain more than one recoverable metal.* These may be present as different minerals, or sometimes, one metal may be in solid solution within the ore mineral of another. Silver, for instance, is frequently found dissolved in lead and copper minerals; in fact, the main source of silver is as a by-product from refining these metals after they have been smelted from their ores. Molybdenum, on the other hand, occurs as a specific by-product mineral associated with certain copper ores and must be separated from the copper minerals before smelting. In many ores, such as those of lead and zinc, two metals may be present as co-products of roughly equal value. Such metal associations are not haphazard; they occur in specific geological environments,

*Many ores contain iron in the form of pyrite gangue, but this iron is not recoverable.

**Table 2.1**  Metal associations.

| Main product | Co-product or by-product as a separate mineral | By-product in solid solution |
|---|---|---|
| lead | zinc | silver |
|  |  | bismuth |
| zinc | cadmium | cadmium |
|  |  | germanium |
|  |  | gallium |
|  |  | indium |
| copper | molybdenum | gold |
|  | cobalt | silver |
|  | zinc | tellurium |
|  | zinc + lead | selenium |
|  | gold |  |
| gold | uranium | silver |
|  | antimony |  |
|  | copper |  |
| nickel | copper |  |
|  | platinum |  |
|  | cobalt |  |
| tin | tungsten |  |
|  | copper |  |
| molybdenum |  | rhenium |
| silver | lead |  |
|  | copper |  |
|  | gold |  |

and a metal may even have different associations in different geological conditions. Examples of associations are given in Table 2.1

Some minerals may have more than one metal in solid solution. The silver content of lead, for instance, depends on the presence of bismuth, as silver cannot be in solution without it. Molybdenum sulphide, itself a by-product, has its own (dissolved) by-product, rhenium. In addition to rhenium, many minor metals have no source other than by-production; cadium, indium, tellurium and selenium are examples.

## 2.2  The ore minerals

### 2.2.1 Native metals

Few metals occur native; even those that do have, with few exceptions, other mineral forms. Gold is by far the most important of them; nearly all is mined as native metal. Some native platinum is mined too, usually alloyed with palladium and osmium, but native metal is not the main source. Native silver also occurs, locally in considerable quantity, but it is not generally an important ore mineral. Native copper metal was of considerable importance during the Chalcolithic and Early Bronze Ages and, even in this century, was mined near Lake Superior in the USA, although the ores are now exhausted. Even as late as 1963, 20 tonnes were mined in Iran: industrially, native copper is now of little significance.

Mercury, bismuth, antimony, arsenic, and even zinc are occasionally found native, as is iron, (although very rarely, and always nickel-bearing). However, most native metals can exist only under very limited conditions. Gold and platinum are exceptions; they are so stable that they can concentrate during sediment transport to form placer deposits. The others cannot.

### 2.2.2 Primary oxide ore minerals

A few ore minerals occur as simple oxides of a metal. Among the most important are cassiterite and haematite. Cassiterite is the main tin mineral, colloquially known as tinstone. Basically, colourless stannic oxide ($SnO_2$), it usually contains sufficient iron to discolour it from yellow to black. Haematite is ferric oxide ($Fe_2O_3$) and is one of the principal iron ores. It has several pseudonyms, depending on its form, including kidney ironstone and specularite.

Some mineral oxides are more complex, including another iron ore, magnetite, sometimes known as lodestone owing to its strong magnetism. It is ferrous-ferric iron oxide ($FeO.Fe_2O_3$, or $Fe_3O_4$) and closely resembles chromite, the only chromium ore mineral. Chromite is ferrous chromic oxide ($FeO.Cr_2O_3$); despite its chemical and visual similarity to magnetite, it is not magnetic. Some oxides are hydrated, such as limonite, an iron mineral found in many geological environments. Limonite is usually given the chemical formula $Fe_2O_3.1\frac{1}{2}H_2O$, but it is really a mixture of several hydrated iron oxides and has no specific crystalline form. Like limonite, bauxite is also a mixture of hydrated oxides; it is virtually the only ore of aluminium and usually given the approximate formula $Al_2O_3.2H_2O$. Its orange to red-brown colour results from the variable amount of hydrated iron oxide which is always present.

There are a number of other primary oxide ore minerals. Some, such as uraninite (pitchblende) may, like magnetite, be mixtures of two oxides of the same element, but others are more complex with numerous substitutions of the original elements by related elements. Samarskite, an yttrium-niobium oxide, is perhaps an extreme example, but it illustrates the point. Its formula should be $YNb_2O_6$, but its composition is actually closer to $(Y,Ce,U,Ca,Fe,Pb,Th)(Nb,Te,Ti,Sn)_2O_6)$. Substitutions may lower the value of a mineral as an ore as in chromite, where aluminium substitutes for chromium ($FeO.(Cr.Al)_2O_3$); or may enhance it, for instance in tetrahedrite, an important silver mineral, where silver partly replaces copper ($(Cu,Ag)_{12}Sb_4S_{13}$).

Some oxygen-bearing minerals are salts. Zircon, for instance, is zirconium silicate ($ZrSiO_4$), beryl, beryllium aluminium silicate ($Be_3Al_2Si_6O_{18}$). In some minerals it is the acid radical which is the important part. The two tungsten minerals wolframite ($(Fe,MN)WO_4$) and scheelite ($CaWO_4$) are examples; they are iron-manganese tungstate and calcium tungstate respectively, and it is the tungstic acid ($WO_3$) which is recovered from them.

### 2.2.3 Sulphides

Sulphides, the result of the chemical combination of metals with sulphur, form one of the most important groups of ore minerals. Many of them are major base metal sources, that is, sources of non-ferrous and non-precious metals. Some have simple compositions, for example:

| | | |
|---|---|---|
| galena | PbS | the most important lead mineral |
| sphalerite | ZnS | the most important zinc material |
| chalcocite | $Cu_2S$ | an important copper mineral |
| acanthite | $Ag_2S$ | an important (low temperature) silver mineral |
| molybdenite | $MoS_2$ | the only molybdenum ore mineral |
| stibnite | $Sb_2S_3$ | the most important antimony mineral |
| pyrite | $FeS_2$ | a common gangue mineral, abundantly associated with many sulphide ores; also a source of by-product sulphur. |

Other common sulphide ore minerals are more chemically complex:

| | | |
|---|---|---|
| chalcopyrite | $CuFeS_2$ | the most important copper mineral |
| bornite | $Cu_5FeS_4$ | the second most important copper mineral |
| pentlandite | $(Ni,Fe)_9S_8$ | an important nickel mineral |
| pyrrhotite | $Fe_{1-x}S$ | another common sulphide gangue mineral; one form is magnetic, although less so than magnetite |

There are many other sulphide minerals, and most metals have a sulphide form although it may not be important. Even tin is occasionally found in sulphide form, combined with copper and iron as stannite ($Cu_2FeSnS_4$). Many sulphides contain other sulphides in solid solution. Galena, for instance, holds silver as the exsolved high temperature sulphide argentite ($Ag_2S$), with bismuthinite ($Bi_2S_3$) and sometimes even stibnite. All are reduced to metal when the galena is smelted, and must be extracted to soften the lead before it can be sold. Even pyrite and pyrrhotite may contain useful elements, and more than half the world's cobalt is extracted as impurities in these two gangue minerals where they occur in copper ores of the African Copper Belt.

### 2.2.4 Some other '-ides'

Some metals which combine with sulphur also combine with arsenic to form arsenides, such as the nickel arsenide niccolite (NiAs), and the platinum arsenide sperrylite ($PtAs_2$). Metals which form arsenides may also form sulpharsenides; cobalt forms cobaltite (CoAsS), iron, arsenopyrite (FeAsS). Sulphantimonides also occur, such as the ruby silver mineral pyrargyrite ($Ag_3SbS_3$). In some of these sulphosalts, antimony may partially or wholly replace arsenic to produce an isomorphous mineral series. Two such series are collectively known as the grey coppers; their best-known members are enargite ($Cu_3(As,Sb)S_4$) in one group and tetrahedrite ($Cu_{12}(Sb,As)_4S_{13}$) in the other.

In addition to these important associations, precious metals can combine with selenium, tellurium, and even bismuth. Examples are the gold-silver tellurides, petzite ($(Ag,Au)_2Te$) and calaverite ($(Au,Ag)Te_2$), and the bismide maladonite ($Au_2Bi$). Although only minor ore minerals, they can be locally important, as the Colorado town called Telluride clearly shows.

## 2.3 Supergene alteration and enrichment

During erosion an ore body is brought closer and closer to the surface until it is eventually exposed. If it is a sulphide ore, the outcrop does not glisten in the sun with shining crystals of galena or chalcopyrite, as many seem to expect. All that is usually seen is a reddish-brown cellular mass of limonite called gossan, left from the alteration of the sulphides when brought into the oxidizing environment between water table and surface (Fig. 2.1). This supergene alteration leaches soluble elements from close to the surface and reprecipitates them lower down to form zones of secondary enrichment where metal values are enhanced, both above and below the water table. The importance of gossans to prospecting has been known since the Bronze Age, but it is astonishing how many newly-graduated geologists still expect to find unaltered sulphides in outcrops. That can occur in cases of very rapid erosion, but it is very rare. Figure 2.2 illustrates the general principles of oxidation.

### 2.3.1 Oxidation

Oxidation occurs above the water table. It is a biochemical process aided by the presence of the iron sulphide, pyrite. Without pyrite, oxidation still occurs but less

CENTIMETRES

**Figure 2.1**
Red-brown gossan from a lead-zinc-silver ore body in eastern Turkey.

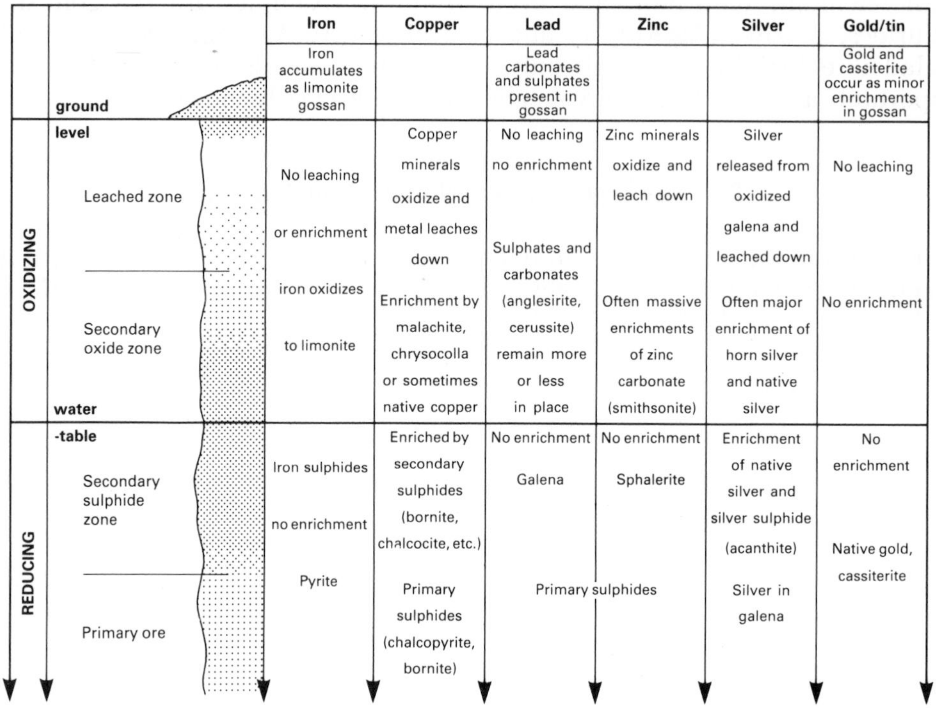

| | | Iron | Copper | Lead | Zinc | Silver | Gold/tin |
|---|---|---|---|---|---|---|---|
| | ground | Iron accumulates as limonite gossan | | Lead carbonates and sulphates present in gossan | | | Gold and cassiterite occur as minor enrichments in gossan |
| OXIDIZING | level | | Copper minerals oxidize and metal leaches down | No leaching no enrichment | Zinc minerals oxidize and leach down | Silver released from oxidized galena and leached down | No leaching |
| | Leached zone | No leaching or enrichment | | | | | |
| | | iron oxidizes | Enrichment by malachite chrysocolla or sometimes native copper | Sulphates and carbonates (anglesirite, cerussite) remain more or less in place | Often massive enrichments of zinc carbonate (smithsonite) | Often major enrichment of horn silver and native silver | No enrichment |
| | Secondary oxide zone | to limonite | | | | | |
| | water | | | | | | |
| REDUCING | -table | Iron sulphides | Enriched by secondary sulphides (bornite, chalcocite, etc.) | No enrichment Galena | No enrichment Sphalerite | Enrichment of native silver and silver sulphide (acanthite) | No enrichment |
| | Secondary sulphide zone | no enrichment | | | | | |
| | | Pyrite | Primary sulphides (chalcopyrite, bornite) | Primary sulphides | Primary sulphides | Silver in galena | Native gold, cassiterite |
| | Primary ore | | | | | | |

**Figure 2.2**   A comparison of the oxidation of ores of different metals, and their secondary oxide and sulphide minerals.

easily and with slightly different results. The chemical reactions are outlined in Figure 2.3. Essentially, pyrite in the oxidation zone breaks down with the help of the bacterium *Thiobacillus ferrooxidans* to produce first, ferrous sulphate (and some sulphuric acid), and then ferric sulphate and ferric hydroxide. Ferric hydroxide is insoluble; it precipitates, then hydrolyses to limonite to accumulate as gossan. Ferric sulphate is a powerful oxidant; it breaks chalcopyrite down to copper sulphate and, in the process, is itself reduced back to ferrous sulphate. Sulphur liberated during the reaction is oxidized to more sulphuric acid to continue the reactions; the liberated iron joins the ferrous-ferric cycle.

Similar reactions occur with lead-zinc ores except that oxidized lead compounds are poorly soluble and remain more or less in place. However, silver dissolved in the galena is solubilized as sulphate and separates from the lead by percolating downwards. Zinc sulphate is mobile too and also percolates away. Tiny blebs of gold sometimes occur in pyrite and chalcopyrite. They cannot be recovered directly but they are released during oxidation and, being insoluble, accumulate with the gossan. A gossan lode of this type overlying copper ore at South Molton in Devon was worked for gold in the 1850s. The Irish County Wicklow placer gold, mined in the 1790s, was probably released from the Avoca copper ores during oxidation, in a similar manner; then removed and reconcentrated by erosion.

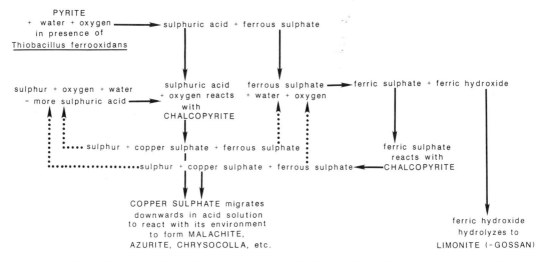

**Figure 2.3** The oxidation of a copper ore. Solid lines show the progress of reactions; broken lines indicate the recycling of products such as sulphur and ferrous sulphate which, after re-oxidation to sulphuric acid and ferric sulphate, react with more chalcopyrite.

### 2.3.2 Secondary (supergene) oxidation enrichment

The metal-bearing fluids produced by oxidation percolate downwards, except in very arid conditions. They react with the environment they pass through and precipitate new minerals above the water table as secondary oxide enrichments. Most commonly they react with carbon dioxide, and the most common secondary minerals are carbonates. Copper forms two brightly-coloured basic carbonates; the green malachite ($CuCO_3.Cu(OH)_2$) and the blue azurite ($2CuCO_3.Cu(OH)_2$). Where carbonate is deficient, copper may precipitate as the silicate chrysocolla ($CuSiO_3.2H_2O$) or, in some conditions, as the red or black copper oxides, cuprite and tenorite. Sometimes, native copper forms, and this is the metal that gave birth to the Bronze Age. Zinc forms a white, or sometimes yellow-tinted, carbonate, smithsonite ($ZnCO_3$), sometimes called calamine by British miners.

Silver does not precipitate as carbonate. It forms secondary concentrations of native metal or the chloride horn silver (cerargyrite, $AgCl$). Silver can form massive secondary enrichments; at one South American mine, it reached 9000 ounces per ton; 60 to 100 oz/t is not unusual elsewhere. Ore such as this from Laurium in Greece financed the Athenian fleet which defeated the Persians at Salamis.

Lead does not form secondary enrichments owing to its poor mobility, although it may form local secondary encrustations of its carbonate, cerrusite ($PbCO_3$). Alternatively, it reacts with other elements to form minerals such as the arsenate mimetite ($Pb_5(AsO_4)_3Cl$), the phosphate pyromorphite ($Pb_5(PO_4)_3Cl$), and vanadinite ($Pb_5(VO_4)_3Cl$), an important source of vanadium. Although the lead sulphate anglesite also occurs, it tends to be uncommon as it readily alters to carbonate.

Copper has the greatest variey of oxidized ore minerals; under arid conditions, it may form enrichments of brightly-coloured sulphates and chlorides such as chalcanthite, brochanthite, antlerite and atacamite. In dry conditions, zinc can precipitate as its sulphate goslarite, but too rarely to be a commercial ore. Where zinc cannot precipitate as a carbonate it forms the hydrated silicate hemimorphite ($2ZnSiO_3.H_2O$), a mineral American miners misguidedly call calamine, a term perpetuated because they unfortunately named another town after it. Calamine is an outdated mineral name best avoided, for it means different things to different people.

### 2.3.3 Secondary (supergene) sulphide enrichment

Not all the metal-bearing solutions produced by oxidation react before they reach the water table. Some metals in solution penetrate below the water table and re-enter reducing conditions. These metals, predominantly copper and silver, precipitate as sulphides with the help of sulphate-reducing bacteria. Copper may precipitate as the simple sulphides chalcocite ($Cu_2S$) and covellite ($CuS$), or react with sulphides already present to produce bornite ($Cu_5FeS_4$), a mineral richer in copper than chalcopyrite. Silver is precipitated as the low temperature sulphide acanthite, or as native metal. Economically, secondary sulphide enrichment can be most important: in some low-grade porphyry copper deposits in the past, it was the only part of the ore body worth working when metal prices were poor.

### 2.3.4 Industrial oxidation

The oxidation of copper sulphide minerals in old mine tailings and waste dumps has long been a minor source of copper metal. Rain water percolates through the dumps picking up sulphuric acid and ferric sulphate from oxidizing pyrite. This leaches out any copper present in sulphate solution, which can be drained away from the base of the dumps into tanks containing scrap iron (Fig. 2.4). The iron replaces the copper in solution and precipitates a muddy cement copper. Now that the importance of bacteria to oxidation has been recognized, the process can be accelerated by providing optimum conditions for bacteria to work in, namely a temperature of about 35°C and shading from sunlight. If there is a deficiency of pyrite in a dump, pyrite tailings are added to ensure the production of ferric sulphate.

## 2.4  Some useful properties of metallic minerals

The physical and chemical properties of minerals, such as hardness, cleavage, magnetism, etc., will be well-known to the reader as useful in identifying minerals. These properties also, however, determine methods of prospecting and beneficiation. Some examples are given below.

| | |
|---|---|
| Hardness | In general, minerals which will accumulate under placer conditions must be hard and abrasion-resistant to survive. The same may be said if minerals are to be concentrated by |

**Figure 2.4**
Tanks for the secondary recovery of copper from copper-bearing solutions drained from old waste and tailing dumps in Turkey. Scrap iron resting on wooden battens replaces copper in solution. Copper precipitates in the tanks as muddy cement copper.

gravity methods of separation based on their different densities. Although heavy, soft, minerals can be concentrated in gravity plants, losses are high. Gold is an exception; it is not a hard mineral, but it is cohesive and, although battered out of shape, does not slime to a fine mud.

Cleavage — Minerals with good cleavage do not concentrate into placers and give poor recovery in gravity concentration plants. They slime.

Density — Minerals with high specific gravities, such as gold (SG 15–19) and cassiterite (SG 7) separate easily from silicate gangues (SG approx. 2–3) in placers and gravity plants.

Magnetism — Only two common minerals, magnetite and pyrrhotite, are sufficiently magnetic to be detected by magnetometry during prospecting. They can also be separated from other minerals by hand magnets. A few other minerals, however, are sufficiently magnetic (para-magnetic) to be separated by high intensity electromagnets.

Conductivity — Some minerals are electrically conductive, and there are a number of prospecting methods based on this property. Oxidation, in particular, produces earth currents, which can be detected with relatively inexpensive equipment.

Wettability — Flotation, one of the principal methods of mineral beneficiation, depends on the surface chemistry of minerals, namely whether the mineral surface can be wetted or not.

Minerals which cannot be wetted will adhere to air bubbles passed through a suspension of finely-ground ore and rise to the surface with· the froth; wetted minerals sink. The wetting capability of the suspending solution can be controlled. Sulphides are generally difficult to wet, sillicates easy.

Radioactivity      Much prospecting for uranium is based on detecting beta-gamma radiation using a scintillometer (Geiger counters are outdated). $^{40}K$ can also be detected to distinguish between granites. Some uranium prospecting now utilizes the daughter element radon as a pathfinder. Radioactive decay of uranium produces radon gas which rises through the ground to the surface soils, where it can be detected with relatively simple equipment (section 6.2.8).

Fluorescence      Although fluorescence under ultra-violet light can be used for detecting some minerals, its prospecting application is limited. It does have some use in mineral sorting after mining.

Solubility      Small amounts of some metals are taken up in groundwater and spread over a wide area of soil during oxidation. Some metals are carried in stream waters and precipiated on fine mineral grains in muds. These metals can be detected in trace amounts and used in geochemical prospecting. Some metals are also taken up by plants, which can be collected and ashed for chemical analysis. A few species of plant even thrive on high metal concentrations, and by their presence can indicate possible ore; California poppy, for instance, flourishes on copper-rich soils. On a different scale, metals can sometimes be leached from their ores after mining, a process termed hydrometallurgy; gold, for instance, can be leached by cyanide solutions, silver, zinc, copper and nickel can be treated by other methods. Metals can even be leached from underground by pumping suitable solvents into the ground and returning them to the surface. Solution mining is still in the development stage for metals, but has long been used to recover salt.

## 2.5  Gangue minerals

Gangue minerals form the part of the ore that must be removed before smelting. Some may have an industrial use, and it is interesting to note that at one time in Britain most fluorite produced (calcium fluoride, $CaF_2$) during lead-zinc mining was dumped as waste. More recently, with new methods of steel making, steel companies have made a concerted search for fluorite for use as a flux. Old mine dumps have been re-treated and old mines re-opened. Any lead and zinc recovered is now the by-product.

In the study of ore deposits, the gangue minerals can give many leads to the conditions of deposition. For instance, tiny bubbles of liquid are trapped in some of them during crystallization. This liquid is the original ore fluid, and under the microscope it can be seen that the tiny cavities containing these fluid inclusions are not completely full; both liquid and vapour phases are present. By heating polished specimens of the mineral to several hundred degrees on a heating stage under a microscope, the temperature can be noted when the liquid expands to fill a cavity. This is the temperature at which the gangue mineral formed, on the assumption that the inclusion was full when the mineral cyrstallized. By freezing the inclusion on a freezing stage, the salinity of the fluid can be estimated. Similar determinations can be made with some ore minerals.

The gangue of an ore is seldom simple. If it is basically rock it will show specific types of alteration; if it is vein material, the combinations of minerals present and their order of deposition are all pertinent. To the ore geologist, the gangue is almost as important as the ore minerals themselves.

## 2.6  Industrial minerals

Industrial minerals will be discussed in more detail later (Chapter 8). Many bulk constructional minerals are common rocks such as granite, limestone, and slate. Other useful minerals are less common, and include gypsum, anhydrite, salt, and diatomite, although where they do occur, they must do so in very considerable quantity if they are to be of any use. Some, such as fluorite, meerschaum, barite, and mica are also uncommon, and are found mainly in relatively small deposits or require considerable processing before they can be sold. Industrial minerals do not receive the attention they deserve and must always be kept in mind when looking at the geology of an area.

## 2.7  Studying minerals

Minerals are the bricks and mortar of a mineral deposit and it is impossible to appreciate ore without knowing something about them. Look upon them as more than just inert chemical compounds; regard each as a material from which things can be made and find out what those things are. Find out also their values either as concentrates or products. How is each material normally sold and what countries produce it? When you look at minerals from these aspects, they take on a personality of their own and become easier to understand.

The best source for much of this information is from technical journals in libraries. The *Mining Annual Review* summarizes world markets for each commodity; it also includes prices, uses, mining, and prospecting methods. Prices of metals traded on the London metal exchanges are published daily under Commodity Markets in the quality newspapers. Other sources of information can be found in the references at the end of this book. A warning, however, is needed: many museums have extensive displays of ore minerals but unfortunately they tend to exhibit exotic and impressive specimens which are rarely found in a mine. Run-of-mine ore is seldom shown, so that the public have distorted ideas of what ore really looks like. This is only too obvious in films and on television; try to visit a few mines to see what it really does look like.

# CHAPTER 3

# Ores and sedimentary rocks

Ore deposits can be classified into two broad groups. Syngenetic ores were deposited at the same time as the rocks enclosing them, epigenetic ores were deposited later than the rocks in which they are found were formed. Syngenetic ores are stratiform, that is, they follow the general stratification of their host rocks (Fig. 3.1a). Epigenetic ores can be stratiform too if they have replaced a stratum or have been emplaced between two bedding planes, but more usually epigenetic ores follow fractures, joints, faults and other weaknesses and cut across sedimentary or other primary layering (Fig. 3.1b). Some ores occur only within a specific stratum in an orefield; they are stratabound. Stratabound ores may be stratiform (Fig. 3.1c), or they may cut the stratum in any direction provided that they do not transgress into adjacent strata (Fig. 3.1d).

### 3.1  Placer deposits

Placer (pronounced plasser) deposits are typically syngenetic. They may be alluvial placers, formed during river development, or beach placers formed along the sea shore. The name is derived from the Spanish *plaza* (a place) and its present spelling reflects the dubious literacy of the prospectors who flocked to the early American West! Most known placers have been formed during recent cycles of erosion but there are a few — and very important ones too — which are fossil placers. Such deposits were buried by sedimentary or volcanic materials immediately after their formation which protected them from erosion and so, although often folded and metamorphosed, they have been preserved until the present day. The Witwatersrand gold ores in South Africa and the Blind River uranium ores of Canada are major Precambrian examples of such palaeoplacers. The deep leads of Australia and California, where alluvial placers were buried by Tertiary lavas and tuffs, are smaller and younger.

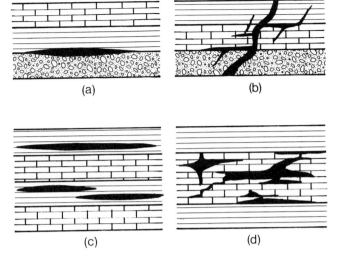

(a)                                    (b)

(c)                                    (d)

**Figure 3.1**
(a) A syngenetic stratiform deposit; (b) is an epigenetic deposit, clearly later than the rocks enclosing it; (c) shows stratabound stratiform ore bodies which could be either syngenetic or epigenetic; (d) shows an example of an epigenetic stratabound deposit.

### 3.1.1 Placer minerals

For a mineral to survive under placer conditions it must not oxidize, it must be insoluble, and it must resist the abrasion it will suffer from the coarser materials of the river or shore bed. Minerals with good cleavage, such as galena, cannot survive, they slime to mud-size particles. However, a placer mineral need not be hard; gold is soft but it is also cohesive and although flattened and deformed to tiny, flat, scaley particles by continual pounding by pebbles in the river bed, it survives. Contrary to the impression given by the film industry, large nuggets are rare. Nuggets are defined as pieces of gold large enough to be heard when dropped into a gold pan; most placer gold is in flat lentil to pin-head sizes, or even finer.

To concentrate well, a placer mineral should have a moderately high density relative to the rock fragments which constitute the remainder of the bedload. Cassiterite (tinstone), with a specific gravity of 7, a hardness of 6, insoluble and lacking cleavages, is an ideal placer mineral; placers form the bulk of all tin production. Nevertheless, many minerals with lower densities, such as the titanium oxide rutile (SG 4.3) and even diamond (SG 3.5) concentrate in placers. The term concentration to describe a diamond placer may appear a misnomer when a viable gravel may contain less than 50 parts of diamond per billion of gravel, but this is still hundreds or even thousands of times more than a normal gravel would have.

Placers produce many of the minerals we use. Most tin and gold and some platinum comes from them; so do the bulk of all diamonds, especially industrial stones, and many other gemstones; and also a wide range of other useful minerals, such as rutile, zircon and garnet, though these are largely from beach placers. Even appreciable amounts of iron ore are recovered along the coasts of Japan and New Zealand.

### 3.1.2 Formation of placers

Placer deposits are formed by the erosion of ore bodies or even merely of rocks

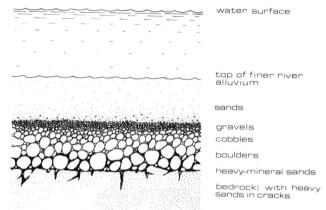

water surface

top of finer river
alluvium

sands

gravels

cobbles

boulders

heavy-mineral sands

bedrock: with heavy
sands in cracks

**Figure 3.2** A cross-section through a simple alluvial concentration. The heavy-mineral sands accumulate at the base of the coarser material and even penetrate the bedrock of the river floor.

containing higher than average amounts of useful minerals. In the latter instance, placer concentration is sometimes the only way in which minerals contained in such rocks can become viable. A river does not have to cut the source rock itself for, during erosion, all material moves down-slope towards the drainage, either washed there by run-off or carried by soil creep. Once within the drainage system, heavier mineral grains are sorted from lighter; small grains of high density travel with larger but less dense granules and pebbles of rock material. These small heavy grains slip down between pebbles as gravel moves down stream until they reach the bottom of the river bed. Some very heavy grains may even penetrate deeply into cracks, fissures and pot-holes in bedrock (Fig. 3.2). Placer minerals concentrate best where the coarsest gravels accumulate, that is, where there are reductions in stream velocities at point bars, or where the streams widen, converge or debouch into lakes (Fig. 3.3). Large placers may occur where

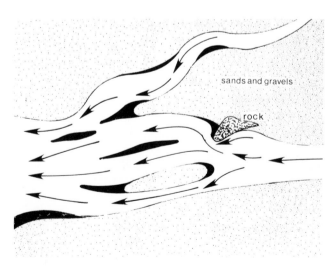

sands and gravels

rock

**Figure 3.3** Positions in a river where concentrations of heavy-mineral sands (black) are most likely to be found, i.e. wherever stream velocity drops.

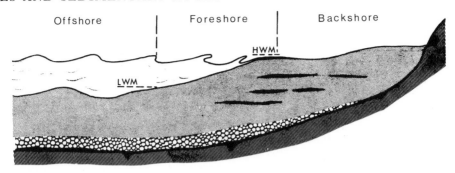

**Figure 3.4** Concentrations in a beach placer. Concentrations of heavy minerals (black) occur on bedrock, and as stringers within sands formed on a storm beach during periods of larger waves.
(After Mero 1965)

extensive terrace gravels have formed, but one should not imagine that the gravels are evenly mineralized; the pay streaks are irregular in size and form, and reflect the constant changes in the history of the river sediments.

Beach placers are formed rather differently. The products of erosion are moved by longshore currents and further sorted on the beaches by wave action. Denser minerals accumulate either in gravels deposited on the wave-cut platform, or in gravel lenses formed on storm beaches and later buried by finer sands (Fig. 3.4). Beach placers are worked on huge scales around the coasts of Japan, Australia, India, Brazil, and many other countries.

Placers are often mined by large-scale dredging. In many cases the pay-gravels are buried by tens of metres of unproductive sands which now form dry terraces well above river level. A large hole is dug, the dredger assembled in it, and the pond flooded. The dredge cuts away the face of the pond in front of it, extracts the valuable minerals from the gravels mined, and then fills in the pond behind it with the sand and gravel tailings (Fig. 3.5). Figure 3.6 shows an ideal dredging

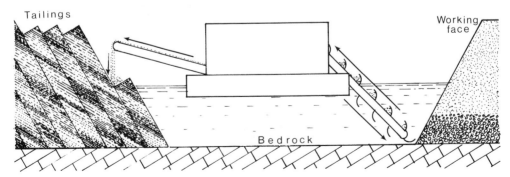

**Figure 3.5** Principle of the bucket dredge. A pond is dug, the dredger assembled in it and the pond flooded; the dredger digs away the gravels in front of it, treats them in its floating plant, and fills the pond behind it with tailings (in effect it moves its pond along with it). A dredge can mine $4 \times 10^6$ m$^3$/year, and dig to 50 m below water level.

**Figure 3.6** Gravels in a tributary of the River Murat in eastern Turkey. If gold-bearing, such a site would be ideal for dredging. The 'river that went out of Eden. . . . where there is gold . . .' (Genesis II) was probably located in this region.

site. In effect, the dredger is a mineral separation plant which moves the man-made pond it floats in along with it. Unfortunately this leaves an unsightly mess, and most other large-scale placer methods are just as bad. Many countries now require companies to rehabilitate the ground they have worked and after a very few years some past mining sites are difficult to recognize as such. Older operations, however, are more obvious (Fig. 3.7). Offshore dredging is done in

**Figure 3.7** Old tailings from dredging on Route 49, California, USA, named after the 1849 gold rush. Note the 'slices of bread' appearance from stacking (cf. Fig. 3.5).

many parts of the world, for tin in Malaysia, Indonesia and Thailand, and for diamonds in south-western Africa. Here, at least, the sea covers the resultant mess.

### 3.1.2 Palaeoplacers

The Witwatersrand basin in the Republic of South Africa is the world's largest placer deposit, despite its great geological age; it produces nearly two-thirds of the western world's gold. Other large palaeoplacers occur in Ontario, Canada, in Ghana, and at Jacobina in Brazil. In Ontario, however, although some gold does occur, the main product is the uranium mineral pitchblende. Uranium is produced in the Witwatersrand too, but only as a by-product. All these deposits are of Aphebian age, approximately 2500 million years old.

The Witwatersrand rocks were laid down in an inland sea and total 7500 m of shales and quartzites (Fig. 3.8). The upper part of the succession is the most important, and the gold is found in thin, pyrite-rich quartz-conglomerate banket, formed in deltaic fans (Fig. 3.9). Associated with banket are bands of carbon a few centimetres thick. These were once algal mats which fringed the deltas and, like the banket itself, they contain both gold and uranium.

The gold was eroded from greenstones in the Swaziland group of basement rocks which surround the basin, where they had been intruded by granite; the uranium came from the granites themselves. The oxygen-poor atmosphere of the age largely prevented the uranium (normally easily oxidized and solubilized) from going into solution and it, like the gold, travelled as detritus to the inland sea. The great thickness of sediment in the basin is accounted for by continual uplift of the

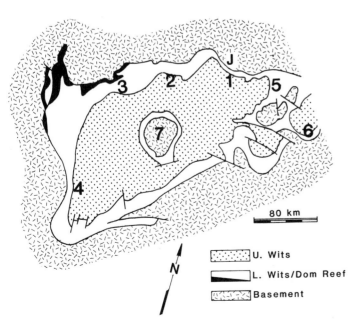

**Figure 3.8**
The Witwaterstrand basin. The various goldfields are:
**1**, Central Rand;
**2**, Far West Rand;
**3**, Klerksdorp;
**4**, Orange Free State;
**5**, East Rand;
**6**, Kinross;
**7**, Vredefort Dome;
**J**, Johannesburg.
The geology is shown with the overlying rocks removed, i.e. Ventersdorp, Transvaal and Karroo Groups. The Witwatersrand Super-group crops out only in the northern part of the basin, and is buried by 1000 m of later rocks in the south. The Upper Division is the gold-producer (compiled from various sources).

80 km

N

U. Wits
L. Wits/Dom Reef
Basement

**Figure 3.9**
Witwatersrand banket.
The pebbles of white
and bluish quartz are
small and ill-sorted. The
matrix consists of finer
quartz and abundant
pyrite. Banket means
'almond cake' in Afri-
kaans, which the iron-
stained outcrops are
said to resemble.

10cm

land by basin-margin faults; the deltaic sediments debouching into the basin were continually re-sorted owing to these rejuvenations, and further winnowed by longshore currents (Fig. 3.10). From the evidence of the carbon bands, it appears that some uranium, and even some gold, was taken into sea water solution to be re-precipitated by the algal mats. Whether the gold travelled far in solution or was merely leached from gold-bearing conglomerates immediately below the mats is debateable. The gold in the carbon bands is native metal; the uranium, however, has reacted with the carbon to form thucolite, a uranium carbide with some thorium, hence Th-U-C-olite. Pretorius (1975) gives an excellent summary of current theories on the origin of Witwatersrand gold.

## 3.2  Residual deposits

Tropical weathering results in the accumulation at surface of the heavier and insoluble components of rocks, whilst lighter and more soluble particles are carried away. Ferric and aluminium oxides form most of the material left behind, cemented into a hard lateritic duricrust. In this way, laterites have formed over huge areas of Africa, India, and South America. On a smaller scale, in both tropical and more temperate regions, eluvial, deposits of heavy, insoluble minerals such as tinstone, are found around the sub-outcrops of mineralized veins where lighter rock and vein materials have been eroded away.

### 3.2.1 Lateritic mineral deposits

Economically, the most important laterites are bauxites: bauxite is a blanket term

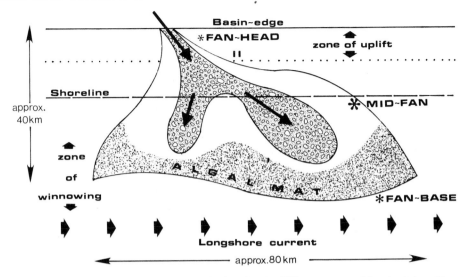

**Figure 3.10** The formation of a deltaic fan in the Witwatersrand basin (after Pretorius 1975). Continuous uplift through faulting at the basin edge results in re-sorting of material deposited. Longshore currents winnow material further. The coarse material is shown by the pebble pattern, the algal mat by the finer pattern. Asterisk sizes indicate the relative gold values.

to cover those laterites which are especially rich in the hydrated aluminium oxides diaspore, boehmite, and gibbsite ($Al_2O_3$. $\frac{1}{2}H_2O$, and $Al_2O_3$, $H_2O$, respectively). Hydrated ferric oxides are the main impurity, with some silica and other insolubles. Bauxites are formed by the lateritization of alumina-rich rocks which are also iron-poor and contain little free silica. Syenites are typical source rocks. But not all bauxites are formed *in situ*, some have been mechanically transported and re-deposited. Bauxite is almost the only ore of aluminium, although the USSR has used nepheline syenite and alunite in the past to remedy a shortage of bauxite. Australia now supplies 30 per cent of the world's bauxite: Jamaica, Guyana, and Surinam 22 per cent; Guinea 14 per cent Yugoslavia, Greece, Hungary, and France another 12 per cent. The remainder comes from a number of small producers, plus 7 per cent from USSR.

Laterites also contain 80 per cent of the world's reserves of nickel at grades better than 1 per cent Ni. However, because of technical difficulties in extracting nickel from laterite, more than half of the metal at present is mined from sulphide ores. Nickeliferous laterites are formed from the tropical weathering of basic to ultra-basic rocks with a higher than normal nickel content but which, if unweathered, would not constitute ore. The ore minerals are hydrated nickel-bearing silicates, such as garnierite, which, being insoluble, accumulate with the laterite as more soluble elements are leached away. Ore grades are as good as those in igneous-related bodies and, although the deposits are only a metre or so thick, they lie at the surface over huge areas and can be mined cheaply with simple earth-moving equipment. New Caledonia and Cuba both mine nickelferous laterites.

It should not be forgotten that gossans themselves are mini-laterites and that, in addition to acting as guides to mineralization, they sometimes concentrate insoluble minerals from their parent veins which would otherwise be of too low a grade to recover. The gossan gold lodes of South Molton in Devon were of this type. Gossan lodes, however, can never be more than minor sources of metal.

### 3.2.2 Eluvial deposits

Eluvial deposits are merely small concentrations of minerals surrounding vein outcrops. The minerals have been shed into the soils by erosion of the ore body but have so far not been transported more than a few tens of metres from their source at most. To accumulate as an eluvial deposit a mineral must be relatively dense and insoluble, and display most of the characteristics of a placer mineral; indeed, for many minerals, eluvial deposition is merely the start of their journey to a proper placer deposit. However, as transport plays little part in eluvial concentration, minerals with excellent cleavage, such as wolfram, may accumulate in addition to gold, cassiterite, columbite, tantalite, and other typical placer minerals. Even some lighter minerals, such as amblygonite, beryl and gemstones may occur.

Eluvials are a boon to the small prospector. They are rich and easily worked and can quickly give him funds with which to buy the supplies and equipment he needs to prove that a worthwhile ore body exists. Too often a prospector is financially unable to benefit fully from his find because he cannot afford the work needed to demonstrate its value to a potential buyer.

## 3.3  Precipitated syn-sedimentary metal deposits

It has never been seriously disputed that the huge concentrations of iron found in the Precambrian banded iron formations and the oolitic iron ores found in the Phanerozoic, were formed during sedimentation. However, until the 1950s, the idea that stratiform bodies of copper, lead, and zinc sulphides could be formed this way was considered to be improbable. Nowadays, few geologists doubt that sulphide ores can be deposited from metal-enriched sea water. Some deposits are forming in this way even now in the Red Sea, on the Eastern Pacific Rise, and elsewhere. Observation stations have been established to observe metal precipitation in New Britain in the western Pacific and at Santorini in the Mediterranean, and much deep-water research is now being done along the oceanic ridges.

### 3.3.1 Iron ores

The bulk of all iron production is from sedimentary ores; only about 10 per cent is from other types of deposit, namely those associated with igneous rocks. Of the sedimentary iron ores, by far the most important are the Lower Proterozoic banded ironstones, taconites, or itabirites, the names given to the especially iron-rich parts of banded iron formations. Banded iron formation, commonly abbreviated to BIF, covers wide regions in many cratonic areas. It is essentially a chemical sediment of alternating cherty bands and siliceous, iron-rich bands, each band only millimetres to centimetres thick and containing almost no clastic material. A single formation may be hundreds of metres thick. The problem is to explain the source of the huge quantities of iron which, by definition, forms 15 per cent or more of the rock.

A popular idea has been that during the Lower Proterozoic there was deep weathering, resulting in the production of highly soluble ferrous iron owing to an oxygen-poor atmosphere. The iron was flushed out of the weathered rock into the drainage by seasonal rises in the water table. It eventually reached shallow seas where it precipitated as iron silicates, or the ferric oxides, haematite and magnetite. The banding reflects seasonal availability of iron, and precipitation appears to have been at least partly biogenic, for tiny plant-like organisms have been identified. However, there is considerable dispute over how much oxygen was present in the Proterozoic atmosphere, and there is also no evidence that the basement rocks of that period were unduly depleted of iron. Volcanic sources of iron can also be discounted. The origin of the iron, and for that matter the silica too, is uncertain. All that can be said is that the iron must have been transported in the ferrous condition and that low oxygen in the early Proterozoic (Aphebian) atmosphere, combined with high carbon dioxide, probably aided its solution, and that biogenic activity helped in its precipitation.

Banded iron formation can only be used as iron ore where it is particularly iron-rich, and most ore mined has been further enriched by secondary leaching of silica from the ore and by the concentration of haematite by circulating groundwaters. Grades of over 45 per cent iron can be attained. Ore beds are often tens of metres thick and many kilometres long. The most notable occurrences are those of Hamersley in Western Australia, the Lake Superior region of USA and Canada, the Labrador Trough of Canada, the Transvaal of South Africa, several parts of Brazil and southern India, and USSR (Fig. 3.11).

Phanerozoic sedimentary ironstones are also extensive, although not on the scale of those of the Proterozoic. These ironstones are essentially oolitic and may be 10 to 15 m thick and strike for 10 to 25 km. The bodies are low grade and usually too poor in iron to work, but they can rise to as much as 35 per cent iron and, because they are carbonate-bearing, they are self-fluxing so that limestone does not have to be added to the furnace charge for smelting. Unfortunately, their low grade has made them increasingly unpopular in the face of cheaper and better ore from elsewhere, namely from the huge reserves of Proterozoic ores described above. Dahanayake and Krumbein (1986) believe these Phanerozoic iron ores were probably formed by the rapid extraction of iron from sea water by fungal mats growing in shallow lagoons surrounded by tropical forests. The ooides are not, in fact, interclasts as once supposed, but authigenic biogenic grains developed within the mats.

In Britain, ironstones occur in the Jurassic rocks of eastern England, but the huge open pits are no longer worked. In western Europe the minette ores of Alsace-Lorraine and the Salzgitter ores of Germany are still worked, but by no means do they thrive. Similar ores occur in the Çamdağ of Turkey although they have not been mined. The Clinton iron ores of USA are more extensive and stretch sporadically from Alabama to the north of New York State. The Clinton ores are older than those of Europe (Silurian) but their grade is much the same (30–35 %

**Figure 3.11**   Location of Precambrian banded iron formation ores (BIF).

Fe), and the mines have suffered the same fate as their European counterparts in the face of competition from other ores.

### 3.3.2 Synsedimentary sulphides in black shales

Not long ago, any suggestion that copper, lead, and zinc sulphide ores could be deposited directly on the sea floor from sea water was considered to verge on the neptunism of early geological science. Stratiform ore bodies, such as the German Kupferschiefer and the African Copper Belt, were unquestionably hydrothermal replacements of the country rocks by fluids from magmatic sources. The Germans were the first to argue that fish bones in the Kupferschiefer had been sulphidized before being broken by lithification of the shale. The answer to this was that diagenetic pyrite was possible, but it was replaced by epigenetic base metal sulphides at a much later date. Garlick and Davis deserve credit for recent acceptance of syngenetic sulphides. Working for Selection Trust in the Zambian Copper Belt in the later 1940s, they showed that copper sulphides were an integral part of the sediments, sulphide particles reflecting all the normal structures expected in unconsolidated muddy sediments, including slumping, ripples, and load casts. At much the same time Haddon-King at Broken Hill had been thinking on similar lines in Australia, but using different evidence. The Australian Baas-Becking Institute carried the work further by directing their energies to resolving the problems of precipitating metals from sea water.

The Bass-Becking Institute demonstrated experimentally that metals could be accumulated on the sea floor by sulphate-reducing bacteria living in the upper parts of sea-floor muds; metal concentrations in sea water as low as half a part per million were enough. Bacteria took the metals into their systems as sulphides by reducing natural sulphate in sea water. Their bodies could accumulate up to 3000 ppm of base metal and 20,000 ppm of iron as sulphides; when they died they enriched the muds they lived in. For the sulphate-reducing bacteria to thrive, reducing conditions are needed on the sea floor. This is the reason why biogenic synsedimentary ores occur in black carbonaceous shales.

There are many syngenetic sulphide deposits around the world. One of the most studied is McArthur River, sometimes called HYC (Here's Your Chance!), in Northern Territory, Australia. HYC has been studied in great detail because, despite its Proterozoic age, it is relatively unmetamorphosed. It contains 200 million tonnes of sulphide ore, averaging 10 per cent zinc, 4 per cent lead, 0.2 per cent copper, and 45 grams (1½ Troy oz.) per tonne silver. The ore averages 55 m thick and occurs in grey to black pyritic shales and siltstones. The sulphides appear to be biogenic according to isotopic evidence quoted by Hutchison (1983), although the sea water from which the metals were extracted may have been originally enriched from volcanic sources. Despite its grade and tonnage, HYC cannot be worked owing to technical difficulties in concentrating the ore.

The Kupferschiefer may also have distal volcanic connections. These ores were first mined in Germany in AD 1150 although long abandoned now. Ore occurs in a thin black shale band less than one metre thick. The same bed continues westwards beneath the North Sea to Britain, where it is represented by the poorly mineralized Marl Slates. Eastwards the band thickens in Polish Silesia, where it is mined extensively.

Ore occurs in the shales as metal-rich zones three or more kilometres wide, underlain by desert sandstones and overlain by, first of all, the Permian Zechstein Limestone and above that, vast thicknesses of Stassfurt evaporitic salt deposits (Fig. 3.12a). Ore is related to those shales formed in what were once semi-enclosed arms of the former Zechstein Sea where stagnant (reducing) water conditions prevailed. The metals may have been derived from the erosion or leaching of volcanic materials deposited to the south immediately prior to the formation of the Zechstein Sea, or from the volcanic activity which occurred in the North Sea High during Zechstein times.

Despite the fame of these ores, based largely on their relatively undisturbed sedimentary condition, the ore deposits are unimposing when compared with others of supposed similar origin. The mineralized zones found in Germany consist of some 15–20 cm of copper-silver mineralization at the base of the shale, averaging perhaps 6 per cent copper and 300 g/t. (10 oz./t.) silver, overlain by 40 cm of shale containing little copper and about one per cent each of lead and zinc. The sulphides were presumably precipitated with the help of bacteria although Hutchison (1983) suggests that hydrogen sulphide from the decomposition of organic matter played its part. The Polish extension to these ores, discovered in 1957, is thicker: 50 million tons of ore averaging 2 per cent copper are known to exist above 1200 m depth (White 1986).

The largest deposits of syngenetic sulphides are those of the Central African Copper Belt lying astride the Zambian-Zaire border. The ores occur in a zone some 200 km long by over 60 km wide in strongly folded sedimentary rocks of the Katangan Supergroup of late Precambrian (Vendian) age. Many of the ore bodies reach 15 m thick and persist over many kilometres of strike. They average about

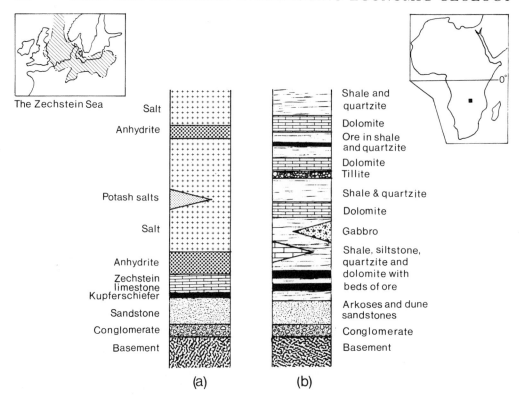

**Figure 3.12** Generalized sequences (not to scale) for the Kupferschiefer (a) and the Central African Copper Belt (b). Both start with a basal conglomerate and desert sandstones. The Zechstein limestone lies above the Kupferschiefer ore shale and is followed by great thicknesses of Stassfurt evaporites. The Copper Belt ores also occur in a shaley sequence, but with arenites and dolomites. The dolomites represent ancient sabkhas and are ore-bearing in Zaire. The gabbros have no connection with mineralization.

3.5 per cent copper, with some cobalt. The Copper Belt as a whole supplies about 17 per cent of the world's copper, and nearly 65 per cent of its cobalt. Despite the vast difference in scale between the Copper Belt and the Kupferschiefer mineralizations, there are two particularly important similarities: the ores are underlain by rocks formed in an arid environment, namely dune sandstones; and they were overlain by rocks containing evaporites, although those in Africa are now largely dolomitized (Fig. 3.12). In Africa, there is a particularly notable feature. If the rocks containing an ore body are unfolded to their state when first formed, the ore minerals are found to be zoned parallel to the ancient shoreline in the following manner:

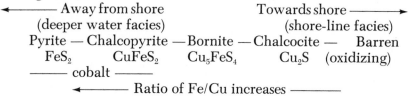

Thus iron increases in the copper ore minerals the further they are from the shore-line until only pyrite (with cobalt) is found; this reflects the differences in solubility of copper and iron chloride. Cobalt occurs largely as an impurity in the pyrite, to the order of about 1 per cent.

Garlick suggested that the copper was derived from the basement schists, gneisses, and granites on which the Katanga rocks were deposited. The basal desert sandstones of the group indicate an initial arid climate; sulphides would therefore have been oxidized to a soluble state above a lowered water table. Humid conditions followed and soluble, oxidized minerals were flushed out of the rocks by the rising water table into the drainage towards a sabkha-fringed basin and onwards into the basin waters, where they were biogenically precipitated.

Many geologists now disagree with simple syngenetic precipitation and have developed more complex models (Jacobsen 1975). For instance, Brown (1978) has suggested that syngenetic mineralization occurs in two stages; in effect, he returns to the replacement of syngenetic/diagenetic pyrite, as first proposed for the Kupferschiefer. He maintains that the sediments were first enriched in sulphur-bearing minerals such as anhydrite ($CaSO_4$) and pyrite. Then, still during the early stages of diagenesis when permeability remained high, the sulphur-bearing minerals were replaced by metal-bearing solutions to form the ore sulphides. Garlick's shoreward zoning of increasing copper content now became a process of more complete replacement towards the metal source.

Further support for replacement, at least in the Copper Belt, is the mineralization in carbonaceous greywackes which cannot be accounted for by simple syngenetic precipitation from sea water. Annels (1979) suggests that methane ($CH_4$) generated from organic matter in the greywackes reacted with anhydrite (which is also present) to produce hydrogen sulphide ($H_2S$) in the well-established reaction:

$$CaSO_4 + CH_4 \longrightarrow H_2S + CaCO_3 + H_2O$$

Hydrogen sulphide will precipitate metals from solution as sulphides (a reaction made use of in analytical chemistry) and Annels assumes the grewacke ores were precipitated in this way from percolating metal-bearing chloride brines. Badham (1981a) has even called these ores secondary for he believes the metals were first precipitated elsewhere to be redissolved and transported through underlying red beds before replacing pyrite and shale clasts in the greywackes by copper sulphides. The source of the metals also remains controversial. Were they leached from basement rocks outside the sedimentary basin, and first precipitated in shoreline sabkhas, and later redissolved in brines, or were they from a deeper source? Jowett (1986), writing of the Kupferschiefer, is another believer in the replacement of early diagenetic pyrite by copper and other sulphides by metal-bearing brines percolating through the underlying red beds. Jowett, however, derives his metals by leaching from volcanic detritus. We are nearly back to where we started! The probability is that no one theory can account for every variation in detail in these syngenetic deposits, which occur in many parts of the world, but with such common features they have at least some similarity of origin for they all show the same general succession, namely:

Evaporites
Algal carbonates
Black shales and greywackes
Desert sandstones
Basement rocks

## 3.4 Epigenetic sulphides with syngenetic connections

Much of the lead and zinc produced today comes from deposits which occur in carbonate rocks, that is, in limestones and dolomites. The ore bodies are found in specific carbonate formations in any one area, but their style is epigenetic; they are stratabound, but not stratiform. The common feature of these deposits is their mineralogy. They contain galena and sphalerite, barite and fluorite, but they are usually poor in pyrite and copper minerals; the galenas are not silver-bearing, and cadium may be a by-product. All appear to have been formed at (geologically) low temperature, between 50° and 180°C, most commonly between about 100–140°C (determined from fluid inclusions). They have been variously called Mississippi Valley type, telethermal, or more appropriately carbonate-hosted.

The Irish deposits are also carbonate-hosted but have marked differences: they are pyrite-rich, some copper and silver occurs, and they contain no fluorite. They are epignetic too, but have syngenetic sulphides associated with them.

### 3.4.1 Telethermal fluids

The term telethermal was devised to explain lead-zinc mineralization in the Mississipi Valley region. This was at a time when all epigenetic ores were presumed to have been deposited by fluids emanating from igneous sources. The problem was that this region lacked igneous rocks. It was initially assumed that the mineralizing hydrothermal fluids had travelled great distances, either laterally or from below: hence 'tele' to indicate distance, and 'thermal' because they were warm. The distance travelled accounted for the low temperatures. It has since been shown that there are no igneous connection; the mineralizing fluids were chloride brines, what oil geologists call formation waters, trapped in rocks during sedimentation and expelled during deep burial in sedimentary basins. They enter porous horizons (aquifers) in the sedimentary pile and move laterally along them, heated by the geothermal gradient (Fig. 3.13).

### 3.4.2 Carbonate-hosted stratabound ores

The lead-zinc ores of the Mississippi basin presented geologists with many problems. Firstly, the ores were stratabound in almost horizontal carbonate formations in a region of little relief. They were blind ore bodies which seldom cropped out or indicated their presence at the surface. Secondly, the ore bodies were numerous but small, irregular and erratic, and seemed to have been deposited without any control by geological structure: they were just there. There was some indication that some ores occurred in breccias, and suggestions were made that the breccias resulted from flexing. As dips were almost zero and

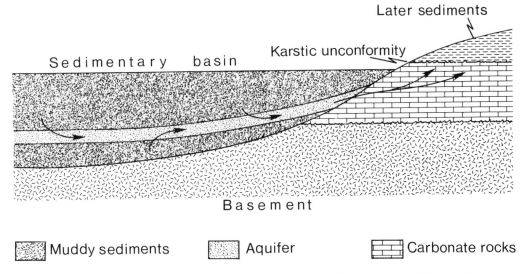

**Figure 3.13** A sedimentary basin with flanking older carbonate rocks. Metals migrate in formation waters from organic muddy sediments via an aquifer, and are carried into the carbonate rocks; they precipitate metals wherever they encounter hydrogen sulphide.

folding non-existent, this view was hard to sustain. Callahan of New Jersey Zinc Corporation (1964) noted the similarity between the mine plans of Jefferson City Mine and maps he had seen of karstic cavern systems of underground drainage. He put his geologists to work; their investigations showed that many ores did occur in breccias, breccias resulting from the collapse of caverns in underground drainage systems after the limestones had been buried by a later period of sedimentation. Independently, Ford and King (1965) had come to similar conclusions at the Golconda mine in Derbyshire. They showed that caverns tended to form in dolomitized Carboniferous limestone above impermeable clay bands (wayboards), and at the dolomitization front where permeable dolomite lay on less permeable limestone. Caverns collapsed to form breccia during burial by Tertiary sediments, but still provided a plumbing system for the percolation of mineralizing fluids and the precipitation of lead and zinc sulphides from them. Barite, fluorite, and calcite also occur with the ore (Fig. 3.14).

Ford and King's work at Golconda mine agreed with the work done by Callahan's geologists on a large number of mines in the USA. More recently the dolomitizing front has become an important factor in prospecting for such ores. Callahan's group also demonstrated that in addition to cavern-collapse breccias, ore occurred in many other permeable features, including coral reefs, and talus and landslide deposits on the basement surface (Fig. 3.14). Vein-like bodies controlled by faults also occur to a greater or lesser extent in different fields, depending on structural history. Derbyshire ores, for instance, are most commonly fault- or joint-controlled. What Callahan, and Ford and King did, however was to show a common origin for the telethermal lead–zinc–barite–fluorite deposits which are found in carbonate rocks in many parts of the world.

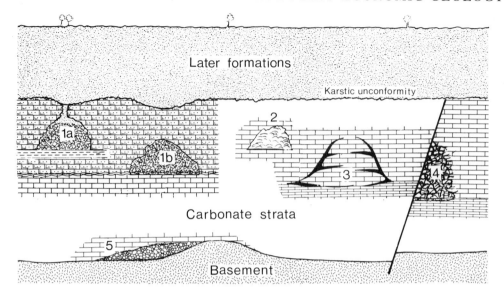

**Figure 3.14** Structures favourable to the deposition of stratabound lead–zinc–barite–fluorite deposits by basinal formation waters. The ore-bearing carbonates lie below later sediments which rest on a karstic unconformity (adapted from Ford and King 1965; and Callahan 1967). **1a**, Collapse breccia in a cavern in dolomite formed above an impervious clay wayboard. This cavern was connected to the karst surface by a sink-hole. **1b**, Collapse breccia filling a cavern formed in dolomite above less permeable limestone. **2**, A permeable reef structure. **3**, Structures resulting in vein-like rakes and flats owing to collapse of underlying beds caused by solution-thinning of beds below. **4**, Breccia in the footwall of a fault caused by collapse owing to solution-thinning of beds below. **5**, Scree, etc. on the precarbonate basement topography.

### 3.4.3 Manner of deposition

Telethermal fluids are brines with an isotopic composition which indicates a predominantly meteoric origin (i.e. rain water which has penetrated the ground to great depths), mixed with connate water driven out of sedimentary material during burial in a basin (Bethke 1986). Some organic, shaley, sedimentary material contains appreciable (a few hundred parts per million) enrichment in copper, lead, zinc and iron owing to deposition in reducing conditions; in effect, it is a very sub-grade syngenetic ore. Connate waters liberated from this material during compaction and lithification take a proportion of these metals with them to mix with meteoric formation waters in adjacent, more permeable, rocks. The metals taken are predominantly lead and zinc, because they have greater chloride solubility at the prevailing temperatures. Also taken into the brines are oil droplets and methane formed from organic material in the sediments; these fluids are identical to the formation waters which transport petroleum to its reservoirs (see section 7.1.6 *et seq.*).

Possibly the liberation of metals, oil and gas from the shaley sediments occurs when water is emitted from clay minerals by the conversion of montmorillionite to illite at about 2 km depth, in the manner suggested by Selley (1985, p.200) for the liberation of oily substances (and see section 7.1.5).

The brines migrate laterally along permeable formations within the basin sedimentary sequence by gravity flow along moderate sub-surface gradients resulting from basin uplift (Bethke 1986). Eventually they reach the basin flanks where they may encounter carbonate rocks (Fig. 3.13). The fluids will then follow the plumbing of those rocks, whether joints, collapse breccias, or other openings. They will precipitate their metals as sulphides wherever they meet a suitable sulphur source. The source may be a solution carrying hydrogen sulphide, produced perhaps by the bacterial reduction of gypsum or anhydrite zones within the carbonate rocks. The metal- and methane-bearing brine may even itself react with gypsum (or anhydrite) within the carbonate rocks to produce hydrogen sulphide by that familiar bacterially-aided reaction:

$$CH_4 + CaSO_4.2H_2O \longrightarrow H_2S + CaCO_3 + 3H_2O$$

Thus, in these ores, deposition appears to be controlled by the presence of bacterially-generated hydrogen sulphide in the rocks or in solutions probably derived from nearby rocks.

The formation of carbonate-hosted lead zinc sulphide deposits would appear to need an adjacent sedimentary oil-type basin from which the metals can be obtained. The evidence for this is abundant. The lead–zinc–carbonate mining fields of the USA are surrounded by oil-bearing sedimentary basins, including the Oklahoma, Kansas, Illinois, and Ohio oil fields. Similar relationships occur elsewhere, although the basins may not always be oil-productive; even the Derbyshire lead field has flanking oil-bearing basins.

### 3.4.4 Lead and zinc in Ireland

Ireland became a prime European producer of lead and zinc in the 1960s when sulphides were discovered in Lower Carboniferous rocks. Tynagh, Gortdrum, Silvermines, and Navan were the most important mines developed. The Irish ores are a mixture of epigenetic vein-like deposits, and bedded syngenetic sulphides precipitated onto the sea floor. But even the epigenetic ores were deposited at very shallow depths, as at Tynagh, where porous unlithified limey sediments were replaced. Russell (1975) suggests that the ore-bearing fluids at Tynagh first precipitated their sulphides in the rocks below, then emerged into the oxidizing conditions of the sea floor to precipitate their iron content as syngenetic iron oxides. At Silvermines, however, the fluids did not apparently shed all their base metals before reaching the sea floor; a massive pyrite body containing galena and sphalerite was deposited syngenetically, but, unlike Tynagh, presumably in reducing conditions.

The fluids in the Irish deposits were apparently derived from underlying Lower Palaeozoic rocks penetrated by reactivated deep faults. The fluids rose up these faults to the sea floor, or to the recently-deposited rocks just beneath it, at temperatures similar to those of other carbonate-hosted sulphide deposits described above, or perhaps just a little hotter. They were apparently connate waters without volcanic or any other igneous connections, but presumably mixed with meteoric contributions. The metals were collected either from the sedimentary rocks the fluids came from, or from rocks the fluids passed through before moving up the faults.

## 3.5  Some conclusions

The origin of placer deposits is fairly clear; particulate mineral grains are eroded from weathered rocks, carried by streams and rivers, and deposited in suitable places along the drainage where velocity falls. Alluvial placers are important sources of gold, uranium, tin, diamonds, and some other gemstones. A few problems remain to be solved, such as the role of the algal reefs in gold-bearing Precambrian conglomerates. That the present-day blue-green algae *Chlorella* can extract gold from solution indicates that the algal mats were certainly more than merely mechanical traps for gold. Beach placers sort and concentrate minerals by a mixture of longshore currents and wave action. They are important sources of titanium minerals, magnetite, garnet, and again diamonds.

Sedimentary iron deposits also present few problems to accepting a syngenetic origin. Syngenetic sulphides, however, are more controversial. There is now little doubt that many sulphide deposits are formed by precipitation onto the sea floor from sea water enriched by rivers draining into a sedimentary basin, or by fluids emanating from the rocks below. Precipitation appears to be mainly biogenic, but the origin of the metals is not always clear, nor is the origin of the fluids themselves. The role of volcanism may sometimes be more important in these deposits than we think; this will be looked at more closely in the next chapter.

Finally, we have the carbonate-hosted deposits. The ores are mainly epigenetic, but they have been derived by leaching from syngenetic enrichments of metals in organic-rich shales in adjacent sedimentary basins. Badham (1981b) has even called them secondary deposits. The Irish deposits are rather different in that they are a mixture of epigenetic and syngenetic ores associated with carbonate rock. They have been formed from fluids which have leached metals from rocks deep below them; in some cases, the rocks leached may even have once been igneous, although not actively so during ore genesis.

Syngenetic ores are an intriguing subject for they have the advantage that they have been formed at low pressures and low temperatures and by methods which allow some experimentation in the laboratory, although not always with wholly satisfying results.

# CHAPTER 4

# Ores and volcanic rocks

Although convenient to classify ore deposits into those related to sedimentation, volcanic processes or igneous intrusives, the divisions are by no means clear cut. Some syngenetic deposits are undoubtedly precipitated from sea water enriched in metals by volcanic activity, others, such as HYC and Kupferschiefer ores (3.3.2) have suspected but unproven volcanic connections. Again, porphyry copper deposits (see section 5.1) are intimately associated with intrusive stocks, but these stocks supplied the materials which built volcanic cones on the surface only two kilometres above their tops. Some gold, silver, and mercury deposits are also found in volcanic districts, but they are more conveniently considered with other vein deposits. The groupings used in this book are merely designed to help the reader to relate ore formation to established geological processes; in more comprehensive texts, other classifications are used.

In this chapter we are concerned particularly with sulphide deposits which have an intimate volcanic relationship. Recently there have been a number of attempts to classify these ores, but so far there is not even agreement on what to call them as a group. Some call them sedimentary-exhalative, others exhalative-sedimentary. Here we will call them volcanogenic sulphides. Edwards and Atkinson (1986, p. 108) have summarized how different authors have sub-divided the group. We will first consider two general types of deposit which some geologists consider to be end members of a gradational series. These are those formed at constructive plate margins (i.e. spreading centres) and therefore associated with basalts, represented by Cyprus-type deposits, and Kuroko ores, which are formed in island arcs near destructive margins and related to more acid rocks, namely rhyolites and dacites. There are other volcanogenic ores, such as Besshi types, which fall between these extremes, but they will not be considered here.

## 4.1 Deposits formed at constructive margins

Copper, zinc and iron sulphides may be deposited in the region of oceanic spreading ridges, but such ores can only be mined when they have pushed towards a continental margin, obducted and made accessible on land. There is one known exception; metal-rich muds have been found in recoverable amounts on the floor of the Red Sea.

### 4.1.1  The Red Sea muds

The Red Sea fills a rift developing between Africa and Arabia, although as yet there is no visible basaltic pillow lava on its floor. Along the median valley are a number of sharp depressions up to 2000 m deep. These deeps contain hot, saline-rich brines; some are floored with metal-rich muds. Atlantic II deep, opposite Jeddah, is the most economically promising. Within its mud are oxide zones (with as much as 64 per cent iron as goethite) and sulphide zones. Sulphide zones are also iron-rich, with up to 29 per cent iron; they also contain 2.8 per cent manganese, 10.4 per cent zinc, 2.2 per cent copper and small amounts of lead (figures from Hutchison 1983). The hot brines enter a deep from beneath its floor, cool by mixing with the water present, and precipitate dissolved metal. The hot brines form from sea water percolating through the Red Sea rocks, enriching themselves in salts from the abundant evaporites; they are heated by newly-formed basalts beneath the sea floor, from which they also leach metals. Mitchell and Garson (1976) have suggested that the brine pools lie on transform faults which cross the Red Sea trough and continue in the on-shore rocks. They also note that Bignell (1975) considers that the geothermal gradient alone could account for heating the percolating brines. This seems unlikely, and underlying basalts are more likely to be the cause of both heating the brines and providing them with metals. Why some Red Sea deeps contain metallic muds and others do not, has yet to be explained.

### 4.1.2  Submarine vents and 'smokers'

In the later 1970s, oceanographic investigation by submersibles discovered chimney-like vents emitting plumes of black, or sometimes white, 'smoke'. The black smoke was hot hydrothermal fluid containing fine particles of metallic sulphides; the white type was cooler fluid carrying calcium and barium sulphates. Smokers stand on mounds of massive ore-grade sulphides within the grabens and on the flanks of oceanic ridges. Despite ore-grades, only two mounds have been found of ore-size; most are less than 50 m in diameter. Their importance is the light they throw on the origin of the Cyprus-type ores which are found in many parts of the world. Smokers have now been found at (a) latitudes 13° and 21°N on the East Pacific Rise (EPR), west of the Mexican coast, (b) on the Juan de Fuca ridge at 46°N, west of Portland, Oregon, USA, (c) at the Galapagos Rift and Fracture Zone Intersection (GRAFZI), at longitude 86°W, (d) at 26°N on the mid-Atlantic ridge, and (e) elsewhere. Most research has been done on the EPR.

Chimneys are porous structures, sometimes as tall as 25 m and up to 5 m in diameter, but most are less than 6 m high and only 2 m across. Despite the hot metal-rich fluids they emit, a distinctive and abundant fauna is associated with them, including worm-like pogonophorans a metre long, clams, limpets, polychaetes, crabs and shrimps. Goldfarb et al. (1983) describe the growth of a chimney as starting off as a small cone or column of anhydrite containing a little pyrite and wurzite (a form of zinc sulphide). The cone walls are sponge-like with silica-lined tubes and, although the 'smoking' plume rises mainly from the central vent, some fluid passes out through the walls and some sea water is sucked back in to mix with the hot solution inside. As the cone grows more chimney-like, the vent begins to line itself, from the bottom upwards, with iron, copper and zinc sulphides. This reduces the porosity of the anhydrite walls and, because there is now no longer any mixing with cool (2°C) sea water, temperature within the lower part of the vent rises to 350°C, the temperature of the fluid from below. In its later stages, a chimney is a column of sulphide with only its upper part sheathed in anhydrite (Fig. 4.1). As activity declines, the anhydrite redissolves to leave just the sulphide. Finally, the chimney collapses.

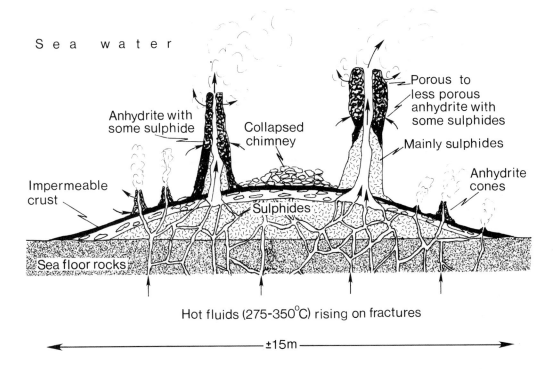

**Figure 4.1** Formation of chimneys and mounds on the sea floor. Fractures on the sea floor emit hot fluids which deposit anhydrite and some sulphides above the vents to form numerous small cones. Most vents soon clog themselves, but a few cones grow to chimneys several metres high. Within the chimney flues, hot fluids mix with cold sea water (which enters through the porous chimney walls, small arrows). Continued deposition reduces wall porosity, and temperatures in the flues rise as mixing with sea water decreases. Iron, zinc and copper sulphides now deposit within the chimney and replace anhydrite to form a tall, largely-sulphide chimney, which eventually collapses. The debris, mixed with anhydrite and sulphides, forms an impermeable crust in the area. The crust is later refractured; more cones form, more chimneys grow and collapse. A mound is built up, helped by extensive sulphide deposition below the mound crust as activity continues. When activity ceases, the anhydrite re-dissolves and only sulphides remain.
(After Goldfarb *et al.* 1983).

The sulphides which build the chimneys are mainly crystalline, although some very fine colloform forms also occur. Some chimneys are copper-rich, others zinc-rich, even within the same group, but all are rich in the iron sulphides pyrrhotite, pyrite, and marcasite. Some Galapagos sulphides contain as much as 27 per cent copper whilst, at the EPR, values of up to 50 per cent zinc have been found. A little lead, and even cobalt, may be present too. The collapse of the chimneys contributes to the sulphides of the mounds they stand on, but they are not the main constituents of it. Goldfarb *et al.* (1983) suggest that mounds grow over fracture zones in the pillow lavas of the sea floor by fluids first building numerous small mutually-interfering cones which block each other off, leaving only a few of the larger ones to survive and grow into chimneys. They stand on an impermeable skin of anhydrite and sulphide beneath which more sulphides accumulate. New movement on the fractures cracks the mound and topples the chimneys; new conelets and chimneys grow and collapse; more sulphides are deposited beneath. The activity is repeated, again and again, and so the mound grows. Sulphides are also deposited as an intersecting vein stockwork in the fractured rocks below. When, eventually, hydrothermal activity ceases, all anhydrite dissolves away to leave a lens-shaped mound of sulphide on which a thin layer of limonitic iron oxides forms by sub-aqueous oxidation.

### 4.1.3 Nature of the fluids

The metal-bearing hydrothermal fluids are formed from sea water which has penetrated to underlying hot basalts and gabbros close to the spreading centre, where it mixed with primary fluids associated with the igneous activity below. Analyses of fluids from Juan de Fuca ridge suggest that there they consist of 95 per cent sea water; the remainder is primary fluid (Chase *et al.* 1985). The metals have been leached from the rocks the fluids passed through, and isotopes indicate that most of the sulphur comes from the same source, with perhaps 10 per cent of it derived from reduced sea water sulphate. Analyses of GRAFZI fluids, however, indicate that there sea water was the predominant sulphur source (Skirrow and Coleman 1982). Temperature of the fluids is in the 250–350°C region.

When smokers were first discovered it was assumed that the plumes of hot fluids rose to about 300 m, carrying tiny particles of sulphide with them, then mushroomed out to form a flat cloud of particles over a wider area. Particles would rain down to form an ore deposit below. Campbell *et al.* (1984) have convincingly argued that such minute particles would not settle; they would disperse. They have also suggested that zoning in mounds with zinc farthest from the vent and copper and iron sulphides closest, is caused by successive replacements in the mound: zinc sulphides replace the anhydrite crust as temperatures rise over 200°C, reprecipitating anhydrite above it; zinc sulphides are replaced in turn by copper and iron sulphides as temperatures approach 350°C, and the zinc is pushed further outwards. This process results, after anhydrite has been re-dissolved, in a zinc-rich outer layer with a copper–iron–rich centre.

So far only two deposit-sized bodies have been found on the sea floor; one is at latitude 13°N and lies 6 km east of the axial graben of the EPR. It is 800 × 200 m in extent, and consists mainly of copper–iron sulphides with a little cobalt. An even larger body, over 50 m thick, has been found at the mid-Atlantic ridge (Pain 1986). As yet, there are no methods of mining them.

These sea floor discoveries do not wholly explain basalt-associated volcanogenic deposits. One problem is the source of metal. Campbell *et al.* (1984) calculate that one cubic kilometre of basalt, completely leached of its metals, would provide $10^6$ tonnes of massive sulphide ore, assuming complete redeposition. But 100 per cent leaching and deposition is unlikely; 5 per cent is more probable. At that figure they calculate that a 100 million tonne deposit such as Kidd Creek in Canada, would need 2000 km³ of basalt, a figure difficult to accept. There is obviously more to it than simple leaching.

### 4.1.4 Cyprus-type deposits

The discovery of smokers and the deposition of sulphide mounds on the sea floor has provided some — but not all — of the answers of the formation of ophiolite-associated copper ores, such as those in Cyprus, eastern Turkey, and elsewhere. The Cyprus deposits occur in a large obducted slice of sea floor which now forms the Troodos Mountains. Gabbros and ultramafic rocks, and a higher zone of sheeted dolerite (diabase) dykes are overlain by basaltic pillow lavas, in turn overlain by clastic sediments (Fig. 4.2) Copper has been worked there since the third millenium BC even the name copper itself is derived from the island via the

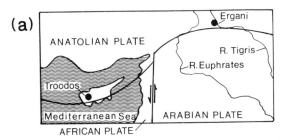

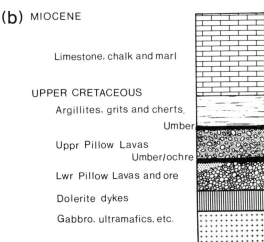

**Figure 4.2**

(a) The relationship between copper ores in the Troodos Mountains of Cyprus and those at Ergani in Turkey to plate boundaries in the eastern Mediterranean. (b) The geological succession in Cyprus. Ore occurs at the top of the Lower Pillow Lavas and is topped by ochre.

Latin *aes cyprium* (metal of Cyprus), later corrupted to *cuprium*. The ores lie between two pillow lava flows and were once thought to be replacements of the lavas by hydrothermal fluids penetrating along their junction. However, Constantinou and Govett (1972) pointed out that a thin umber (iron-rich clay) layer on the top of the Lower Pillow Lava flow and an ochreous (hydrated iron oxide) top to the ore, indicated that both had been sub-aqueously weathered before the Upper Pillow Lava was erupted. The upper lava had flowed over the umber and ochre layers and protected them from further erosion. The ore was deposited largely syngenetically on the top of the Lower Lava. But not all the ore was syngenetic; a stockwork of feeder veins occurs in the lavas below.

The formation of smokers and mounds explains how the ores were deposited and also explains the previously puzzling presence of colloform textures and breccia fragments, which are now known to be chimney debris. Most of the ore, however, is massive pyrite and some marcasite, with chalcopyrite, bornite and chalcocite enriching it towards the top to about 3 per cent copper. Only a little zinc occurs. Most authorities consider these ores were deposited at the graben of the oceanic ridge.

There are about fifteen workable copper ore bodies in Cyprus. Of similar Upper Cretaceous age and associated with the same obducting plate margin are two ore bodies at Ergani Maden on the west bank of the upper Tigris. There the depositional environment was a little different. The ore-bearing fluids rose through the sea-floor rocks on the flanks of the oceanic ridge, some distance from the graben. They rose into wet clastic and hyaloclastic Layer 3 sea-floor sediments which had yet to be fully lithified. The fluids were trapped in the sediments and were unable to form chimneys and mounds; they deposited lenses of massive sulphides containing black chloritic intercalations of the host sediments, with some disseminated ore above and, as in Cyprus, a stockwork of veinlets in the more consolidated rock below.

The Ergani ores were once very much richer than those in Cyprus and, even in the 1960s, grades of 9 per cent copper were worked. Slags in ancient dumps contain 4 per cent copper, suggesting some early-mined ore may have reached as much as 15 per cent. Ergani Maden is the oldest metal working known, and native copper artefacts have been found downstream which have been dated from just later than 7000 BC. Cyprus-type ores also occur in ophiolite regions elsewhere, including Newfoundland and the Philippines.

## 4.2  Volcanogenic ores in island arcs

The ores described in the previous section are found close to destructive plate margins, but they were not formed there. They were formed at constructive margins and transported by plate movement to the destructive margin and obducted onto a continental land mass. The ores to be described next, however, were formed near destructive plate margins and are by-products of subduction. They were formed on the floors of inter-arc basins in island arcs. One type is associated with the earlier stages of island arc formation, with mafic (tholeiitic) rocks, and is called the Besshi or Kieslager type. The other, the Kuroko type, is formed at the later dacitic to rhyolitic stage. Stanton (1978) considers Cyprus, Besshi and

Kuroko ores as a single progressive geochemical series; others disagree. We have already considered the Cyprus end-member; here we will concern ourselves with the other end member, the Kuroko ores.

### 4.2.1 Kuroko ores

Kuroko deposits are relatively small, lens-like, polymetallic bodies, often only 100–200 m across. They occur in groups. Literally, 'Kuroko' means black ore in Japanese; it is a term now used internationally for ores of this type (in fact, the ore bodies are made up of several types of ore, by no means all black). The average ore grade is about 2 per cent copper, 5 per cent zinc, 1.5 per cent lead, as sulphides (with abundant pyrite), and 1.5 g/t of gold (about $\frac{1}{20}$ oz/t) and 100 g/t silver (c. 3 oz/t); up to 2 kg/t of uraninite is occasionally present, and gypsum and barite occur in abundance. Some ores may even have been reworked (i.e. eroded) and redeposited further from the original source.

### 4.2.2 Japanese ores

The type examples of Kuroko deposits are found in the Green Tuff belt of western Honshu, Japan. They occur in a 300 m thick sequence of Miocene tuffaceous and sedimentary rocks in a belt over 1000 km long and 100 km wide; they form relatively undeformed, sub-horizontal sulphide lenses, some 50 m thick. Many are 'blind', lying 100 m or so beneath flat rice paddy. The ores are closely associated with dacitic and rhyolitic lava domes enclosed in volcanic breccias which were erupted — explosively in the early stages — on to the sea floor (Fig. 4.3a). The lowest level of ore is a stockwork of intersecting copper-rich quartz–pyrite veins in silicified tuff breccia. These were feeder channels for ore solutions (Fig. 4.3b). Above this epigenetic mineralization is a syngenetic stratiform bed of copper-bearing pyritic Oko or yellow ore with some zinc and barite. This is in turn overlain by the black stratiform zinc–lead–copper–pyrite Kuroko ore, again with barite. A thick barite bed overlies all, with a thin ferruginous chert sharply separating the ore zone from the tuffs and mudstones which cover them.

### 4.2.3 Formation of Japanese Kuroko deposits

These deposits were formed at a water depth of at least 2500 m by hydrothermal fluids of sea-water origin mixed with some magmatic water. Isotopes indicate that the metals were derived from the magmatic rocks below, and that the sulphide sulphur was from various sources. The fluids deposited a fine precipitate of metallic sulphides as they emerged onto the sea floor at about 220°C. The ore fields within the Green Tuff belt are localized in submarine calderas and Sato (1977) shows the belt lying some 155 km above the westward-dipping Benioff zone, with the East Japan trough some 300 km to the east.

Sato also suggests that basic and intermediate magma generated by movement along the Benioff zone rose into the upper mantle until it reached lighter continental crust, where its buoyancy — due to its difference in density from mantle material — was lost. The magma ceased to rise; it differentiated, and the lighter, more siliceous, volatile-rich fraction then rose through the crust to erupt

(a)
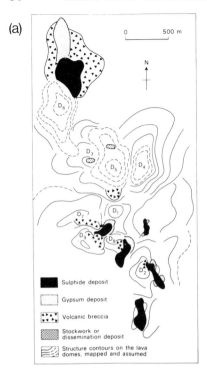

(b)
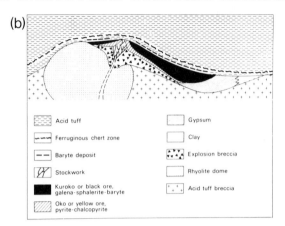

**Figure 4.3**
Kuroko deposits: (a) The distribution of dacite lava domes and Kuroko ore deposits in Kosaka district, Japan; (b) A schematic cross-section through a Kuroko deposit.
(From Evans 1980: 138–9, with permission)

as rhyolitic/dacitic lavas and pyroclastics. The lavas brought ore-bearing magmatic fluids with them; these mixed with sea water percolating beneath the sea floor to form the mineralizing fluid.

### 4.2.4 Kuroko deposits elsewhere

Although Japan is the type area for Kuroko deposits, ores of similar origin occur elsewhere. Colley (1976) gives a review of deposits in Fiji and classifies them as types I to IV, depending on their proximity to the volcanic exhalative centre (Fig. 4.4). He also adds a type V, formed from the erosion of deposits in the shallower water up-slope and redeposited in deeper water. This type is only assumed to exist but ore which might fall into this category occurs at Kushk, in Iran. The Kushk ores are sphalerite shales (Fig. 4.5). They have a fine lamination of sphalerite and shaley material. They show other sedimentary features, and where they have not been recrystallized, the sulphides are of similar size to the sedimentary minerals. The ore bodies are up to 40 m thick and assay up to 50 per cent zinc ( + a little lead) with a small amount of pyrite, enclosed in pyrite-bearing carbonaceous shale. The carbonaceous shale is overlain by brown and green shales containing fine volcanic material, with dolomite above them. The ore-bearing shale lies on rhyolite. Bailey *et al.* (1978) assumed that the three ore phases represented three volcanic surges precipitating the ore minerals, but the three phases might well represent depositions by three closely-spaced erosive periods. Kushk could therefore fall into either type IV or V of Colley's classification.

Kuroko deposits occur in many parts of the world but, because folding and

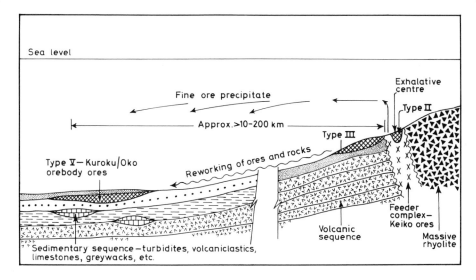

**Figure 4.4**  A classification of Kuroko-type deposits in Fiji.
(From Colley 1976, with permission)

**Figure 4.5**
(a) Sphalerite shale from Kushk, Iran. The pale grey bands are sphalerite, the dark material is carbonaceous mudstone, the very light lenticles are pyrite; very little galena is present.
(b) Pyritic shale from Kushk. The light-coloured pyritic lenses and wisps are composed of clouds of tiny pyrite grains (framboids). All the rock is also pervaded by microscopic pyritic framboids.

metamorphism tend to obscure their origin, they were not identified as such until their distinctive criteria had been recognised in the relatively undeformed deposits of Japan. Because such ores are formed late in volcanic arc history, their chances of preservation are poor, and Colley considers that this accounts for their rarity in older rocks. Yet, they have been found in the Mesozoic of the Pontic mountains of northern Turkey, and in Lower Palaeozoic rocks at Avoca, in Eire, and in the famous Rio Tinto sulphide deposits in Spain. Ores with many of the Kuroko criteria have even been found in the Precambrian Canadian shield.

### 4.3  Other volcanogenic sulphide deposits

Volcanogenic exhalative-sedimentary sulphide ores which are not of Kuroko type occur in many parts of the world. The ores are often zinc-rich, copper-bearing, but poor in lead. They are usually stratiform with a considerable lateral dimension and may show distinct sedimentary features. Their age is commonly Precambrian. Several important ore bodies of this type occur in the Abitibi green-stone belt in western Canada. In the Noranda district, which lies across the Quebec-Ontario boundary, the Kidd Creek deposit contains 150 million tonnes of silver-rich zinc–copper sulphide ore. The silver is mostly native, and cassiterite is an important by-product. The ores are closely associated with rhyolites and carbonaceous argillites, despite the general greenstone environment. Mattagami, in the same greenstone belt, has similar features. Hutcinson (1983) relates this mineralization to metals precipitated from solution in volcano-sedimentary basins during explosive rhyolitic volcanism. Although the ores are largely syngenetic, stockworks of feeder veins occur below. But not all Precambrian zinc-rich, copper-bearing ores associated with rhyolites are necessarily syngenetic; the case must be proved in each instance.

### 4.4  Volcanogenic iron ores?

The huge stratiform deposits of magnetic iron ores at Kiruna in the Precambrian greenstone belt of Swedish Lapland have generally been accepted as the product of magmatic segregation, as have similar but highly-deformed ore bodies at Malmberget, 75 km to the south. The largest ore body — Kiirunavaara — is over 5 km long, averages 90 m wide, and dips steeply. The ore is massive magnetite with a little haematite, plus accessory fluor-apatite which can raise the phosphorus content to over 5 per cent. The geological sequence begins with green-stones over 1950 Ma old, overlain by conglomerates (Fig. 4.6). A great thickness of keratophyres (i.e. soda-trachytes) with some trachytes follow, passing upwards into quartz-keratophyres and rhyolites. These rocks have been dated at 1600 Ma and are metamorphosed largely to syenites and quartz-porphyries. Sedimentary rocks, including phyllitic mudstones, greywackes and sandstones, complete the sequence. The ore occurs mainly as stratiform bodies at the junction between keratophyres and quartz-keratophyres, although the Per Geiger ores lie on lavas just below the sedimentary rocks. Similar but smaller magnetite deposits occur elsewhere in the world, always associated with keratophyres or syenites, and always with accessory apatite.

There is little argument over the source of iron in these deposits. A basic magma is assumed to have cooled in its chamber, with olivine and pyroxene crystallizing out early and sinking to consolidate at the chamber floor. The remaining magma was enriched in silica and iron and, as it cooled, the iron formed oxide droplets which were immiscible with the silicate melt. The droplets were heavy; they coalesced to form larger drops and sank to the bottom of the magma chamber, which was now floored by the newly-formed olivine–pyroxene rocks. The chamber thus contained a large quantity of silicate melt of inter-

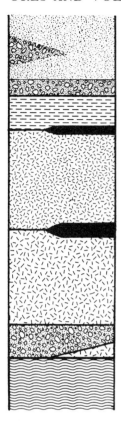

Sandstones and conglomerates

Conglomerate and greywacke

Phyllites

Per Geiger ores

Quartz keratophyres and syenites

Kiirunavaara, etc., ores

Keratophyres and syenites

Conglomerates

Keratophyres

Greenstones, etc.

**Figure 4.6**
The geological succession at Kiruna, Sweden (simplified after Parak 1975). The Per Geiger ores are at the top of the volcanic sequence and could possibly be extrusive. The Kiirunavaara and the less important Luossavaara ores occur at the junction between keratophyre and quartz-keratophyre. Conglomerates immediately above the Luossavaara ores contain cobbles of magnetite, which suggest an extrusive origin.

mediate composition resting on top of a much smaller amount of iron oxide melt. At some stage, the chamber was tapped and the silicate melt rose to the surface to form the great thicknesses of intermediate lavas seen today.

Later, the residual iron oxide melt was tapped, its melting point depressed by volatiles such as the fluorine, which would eventually contribute to the fluorapatite in the ore. The main differences of opinion concern what happened to this iron oxide melt. Was it intruded between lava flows to form stratiform but epigenetic sills of magnetite, or was it erupted as a molten iron oxide lava onto the ground surface in the middle of volcanic activity? Magnetite lavas can occur, as shown by the small flow found some years ago at El Laco in the Andes. The upper Per Geiger ores would certainly appear to be extrusive. The main Kiirunavaara ores, however, exhibit many intrusive features, although the Luossavaara ores, which are on the same strike, are locally overlain by conglomerates which contain cobbles of magnetite identical to the ore. The problem is by no means solved. Frietsch (1978) still maintains the ores are intrusive; Parak (1975) suggests that they are sedimentary-exhalative. The present author favours an extrusive origin. Unfortunately, the intense deformation and metamorphism of both ores and rocks at Malmberget to the south rules out any help in solving the problem from that direction. All that can be said is that similar ores in Missouri and elsewhere, once thought intrusive, have now been shown to be extrusive.

### 4.5  Carbonatites and kimberlites

Carbonatites are small, stock-like volcanic pipes filled with crystalline calcitic and dolomitic carbonates, i.e. essentially marbles. They are associated with alkaline volcanic complexes, with cones formed of phonolite, nephelinite and their related pyroclastics. Carbonatites occur in stable cratons which are about to rift or are already doing so. They have strong affinities with kimberlites, the host rocks of diamonds. Carbonatites first came into prominence in the early 1950s when it was realised that they contained niobium-bearing minerals (niobium = columbium in USA), niobium being needed for alloying in heat-resistant steels used in jet turbine blades.

#### 4.5.1  Carbonatites

A notable advance was made in 1950, when C.E.F. Williams discovered some 200 million tonnes of residual soils resulting from the erosion of the Sukulu carbonatite complex in eastern Uganda (Barnes 1961). These soils contained 0.2 per cent $Nb_2O_5$ in the mineral pyrochlore $[(Na,Ca)(Ta,Nb)_2O_6.(O,OH,F)]$. They also contained 13 per cent $P_2O_5$ as apatite, together with zircon $(ZrSiO_4)$, baddleyite $(ZrO_2)$ and titaniferous magnetite. This appeared to be an ideal deposit for mining by earth-moving equipment. Unfortunately, the fine size of the pyrochlore (45 per cent was below 10 $\mu m$  resulted in concentration difficulties. A number of other carbonatites occur in Uganda but none can be mined. Carbonatites have been worked as hard-rock open pits in southern Tanzania, in Brazil, USA, Canada and USSR, as there the ore minerals are coarser grained. Not all are worked for niobium: Clark Mountain in California, USA, once produced rare earths; the Brazilian Jacupiranga complex, apatite. The most notable carbonatite, however, is Palabora in South Africa. The complex consists of three pipes and produces copper, phosphates, vermiculite (see 8.1.3), hafnium-bearing baddleyite, uranium and magnetite, plus a number of minor metallic by-products.

#### 4.5.2  Origin of carbonatites

Carbonatite is derived by the differentiation of basaltic magma from the mantle, contaminated by crustal materials as it rises along deeply-penetrating weaknesses in Precambrian shield rocks. First, alkaline phonolite and nephelinite lavas are erupted to form volcanic cones (Fig. 4.7); only in the final stages does the carbonate magma rise to block the volcanic vent or pipe. The pipe is surrounded by metasomatically-altered basement gneisses, some converted to ijolite (nepheline–pyroxene rock) in the inner zone. Further afield a soda-rich fenite of alkali syenite composition is formed by loss of silica in the gneisses, and replacement of their feldspars. The diameter of the carbonatite pipe may be anything up to 500 m, but many are much narrower.

#### 4.5.3  Composition of carbonatite

Carbonatite is variable. It may be a marble-like calcitic variety, often with

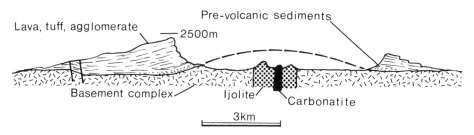

**Figure 4.7** Napak volcano, NE Uganda. The photo shows hills formed from lavas and tuffs remaining after the erosion of the centre of the volcanic cone. The cross-section shows doming in the Precambrian basement gneisses due to volcanic activity. Carbonatite fills the central vent, surrounded by ijolite, an olivine–pyroxene alteration product of the gneisses. Gneisses surrounding the ijolite are fennetized.
(After King 1949)

phlogopite and biotite, coarse magnetite crystals, apatite, and other minerals; or it may be dolomitic. Some varieties contain sodium carbonate. In general, the composition within a pipe varies from place to place, which makes it difficult to use the carbonate for cement making, although Uganda has proved that it can be done. Even carbonatite lava flows occur.

Carbonatites are most interesting rocks. The idea that carbonates could form an igneous body was long resisted. Even when accepted, the suggestion that carbonate lavas could also occur was strongly disputed until the early 1960s when J.B.Dawson witnessed a sodium carbonate flow at Oldinyo Lengai in northern Tanzania. Such flows obviously cannot survive much rain and are quickly dissolved away to contribute to soda lakes. At Lake Magadi in Kenya, the soda is commercially exploited.

Carbonatites are useful sources of minerals, both metallic and non-metallic. They can produce copper, iron, niobium, zirconium, hafnium, uranium, titanium, rare earths, and even by-product nickel, cobalt and gold. Industrial materials include cement-limestone, phosphates and vermiculite. They deserve attention.

### 4.5.4 Kimberlites

'Kimberlite is a very rare, potassic, ultrabasic hybrid igneous rock that occurs as small diatremes (i.e. pipes), or as dykes or sills of limited extent' (Hutchison 1983). It is the rock from which most diamonds are derived. Some diamonds are mined directly from it; most are recovered from placer deposits resulting from the erosion of kimberlite pipes and dykes. A few are mined from placers formed by the erosion and reworking of fossil placers, some dating back to the Precambrian. But not all kimberlites carry diamonds; those that do are the exception, and even those which are mineralized average only about 1/4 of a carat per tonne, i.e. about 50 parts per billion.

Kimberlites, like carbonatites, are formed in the mantle, but they rise more rapidly, collecting xenoliths of eclogite, peridotite and rocks they pass through on their journey to the surface. Like carbonatites, they rise on deeply-penetrating fractures in cratonic regions; Dawson (1971) envisages them as forming dyke-like bodies which explode to the surface at points along their length as mixtures of solid mineral matter and carbon dioxide gas. The escape route forms a funnel-shaped pipe broadening towards the top, filled with fragmented solid kimberlite supported on the expanding escaping gas column as a fluidized system. Wyllie (1979) suggests that the kimberlite is generated deep in the mantle from peridotite enriched in carbon dioxide and water; others, however, believe that the carbon dioxide comes from the lower crust.

### 4.5.5 Diamonds

Diamonds are formed deep in the mantle as high-pressure polymorphs of carbon. They are very much more abundant in the eclogite xenoliths than in the kimberlite itself, probably even those that are found in the host rock have been released from xenoliths. Isotopic ages show that the diamonds are older than the enclosing kimberlite and were already formed within eclogite before the kimberlite formed.

### 4.5.6 Prospecting for diamonds

Most diamond-bearing pipes and dykes are Cretaceous or younger. As would be expected with bodies which almost reach the land surface, their chances of preservation from erosion are poor. Diamonds do, however, occur in clastic sediments of many ages, derived from earlier kimberlites, and these clastic rocks may be eroded, the diamonds released, and new placers formed from them, as in Ghana.

As even workable diamondiferous rocks and gravels contain only 50 ppb or so of diamonds, searching for the diamonds themselves is unproductive, particularly as kimberlite is rapidly weathered to a friable yellowish soil which is difficult to recognize. Therefore, the primary search is to locate kimberlites by looking for 'pathfinders', namely distinctive minerals which occur in kimberlite but which are hard enough to survive erosion and heavy enough to be concentrated to a heavy mineral concentrate from stream gravels by prospectors. Pyrope garnet, chrome diopside and picro-ilmenite are the usual indicators. These pathfinders are looked for in streams near 'diamond' lines, those fracture directions many hundreds of kilometres in extent along which kimberlites occur. Companies jealously guard their own information regarding such lines.

Once indicator minerals have been found, they are traced back to their kimberlite source and then the real search for diamonds begins. In the taiga and tundra regions of Siberia, the Russians supplement this method by taking soil samples, which are analysed for trace zinc; as the contact with a kimberlite is approached, the zinc content of soil rises, to fall abruptly as the contact is crossed. Thus a pipe or dyke can be found even under the overlying soils.

South Africa does not have a monopoly on diamond mining as many believe; it produces most gem stones, but both USSR and Zaire produce more carats, mostly as industrial diamonds. Botswana, Namibia, Ghana, and Angola are also important African producers; Sierra Leone, Tanzania, and the Central African Republic add to the African total. Brazil and Venezuela also mine diamonds, and a recent find includes a very large discovery in NW Australia, coincidentally beside the Kimberley Craton although most of the diamonds occur in lamproite, a potash-rich leucite-bearing lamprophyre, rather than kimberlite. The bulk of all industrial diamonds now produced are, however, synthetic stones (section 8.10).

### 4.6  Beryllium-bearing tuffs

There was an urgent demand for beryllium ore in the 1950s. Beryllium bronze (Cu:Be 97.75:2.25) had long been used as a hard, fatigue-resistant alloy suitable for springs, but the very favourable thermal-neutron cross-section of beryllium also made it suitable for canning uranium rods for nuclear power generation. Furthermore, beryllium is the lightest of all metals, and its structural properties make it potentially ideal for the aerospace industry. Unfortunately, it is a difficult metal to refine to the purity required, and the toxicity of its oxide makes it difficult to machine. There are many other uses, including metal ceramics (cermets).

Beryl [$Be_3Al_2(Si_6O_{18})$] was once the only practical ore mineral of beryllium. It occurred in recoverable amounts only in pegmatites which form small, erratic and rather rare ore bodies (section 5.4). In the mid-1960s beryllium-bearing nodules, 5–10 cm across were found in Pliocene ignimbritic tuffs at Spor Mountain, southern Utah, USA. The nodules were formed from dolomite pebbles picked up by the incandescent ash cloud (nuée ardente) as it rolled downhill. The pebbles were silicified, and mineralized with fluorite, bertrandite ($H_2Be_4Si_2O_9$) and phenakite ($H_2Be_2SiO_4$) by gasses entrained in the hot ashes or by solutions rising into the tuffs from faults below. The huge volumes of poorly-consolidated tuffs are easily open-casted and the nodules screened out for transport to a nearby plant, where both fluorite and beryllium oxide are extracted. There is at least one other similar occurrence in Utah and similar deposits must certainly exist in other parts of the world. Spor Mountain is one more recently-discovered type of ore deposit directly associated with volcanic activity.

## 4.7 Conclusions

The formation of sulphide ore minerals by sedimentary processes was a relatively new concept only forty years ago, but is now generally accepted. Suggestions that many base metal ores could also have been formed by sea floor volcanism also date from much the same period, although many vein deposits had long been considered to be closely related to volcanic activity, especially silver, mercury, and gold deposits. In this chapter we have been concerned mainly with ores formed by volcanically-related emissions and extrusions. In the next chapter we will see how volcanic activity is related to certain vein deposits and how this volcanic activity is really an extension of other ore-forming processes which occur at depth.

# CHAPTER 5

# Ores and intrusives

This chapter covers a wide range of ore deposits, all associated with various aspects of intrusion, although some may also have volcanic affinities. First are the porphyry coppers, ores intimately related to felsic stocks; they too have some volcanic connections. Ores formed by replacement of sedimentary rocks close to intrusions are also considered, as are various vein deposits. Veins may occur either within intrusions or in the rocks which have been intruded, and some veins have a sub-volcanic relationship. Finally, ores formed by segregation within both intermediate and mafic intrusions are described with, in one case, an intriguing alternative.

### 5.1 Porphyry copper deposits

The widely used term porphyry copper deposit is grammatically misleading for it is not the copper which is porphyritic but the rock it occurs in. Porphyry copper deposits are complex, stock-like intrusions which have penetrated to within 3 km of the earth's surface; some are a kilometre across, some more, some less. The rock is typically porphyritic with a fine- to medium-grained groundmass. Composition varies from granite and granodiorite, through monzonite and quartz monzonite, to diorite and quartz diorite. Most stocks contain at least two of these rocks and are cut by dykes of similar composition. The ore is the rock itself and occurs in quantities from 100 to 2000 million tonnes. Because of their size, porphyry copper deposits are usually mined in huge open pits by mass mining; Bingham, USA, for example, mined 130,000 tonnes of ore every day in its prime, plus a further 270,000 tonnes of waste rock overburden (see Fig. 1.2). Copper in porphyries occurs as disseminated sulphide grains, stockwork veinlets and even larger veins, giving an average grade of well below one per cent copper. Pyrite is always present in abundance and molybdenum, a highly priced metal, is a valuable by-product at 0.015 per cent, or less. Occasionally, molybdenum rises to 0.3 per cent to form porphyry molybdenum stocks, with copper as the by-product; Climax and Henderson in Colorado, USA, are examples. Porphyry copper stocks in island arcs, as distinct from those on the continents, are usually low in molybdenum but relatively rich in by-product gold. Some, such as those in Papua New Guinea, were in fact discovered by following up earlier gold finds.

Not all the ore associated with a porphyry copper is in the stock. Ores occur intermittently in the intruded country rocks as veins and replacements for some 10 km outwards from the contact in the well established sequence of:

contact ◄─────────────────────────────► 10 km

porphyry     iron — copper — zinc — lead — silver — manganese

Within the stock, tin, tungsten, bismuth, arsenic, tellurium, selenium, nickel, silver, gold, platium and rhenium form minor by-products. By-product sulphuric acid from the smelting of the sulphide ores may also be saleable; even if not, anti-pollution laws may still require its recovery and disposal, adding up to 30 per cent to the cost of copper production. In low grade deposits such as these, that can be crucial (Aitkin 1985), and see section 8.11.3).

### 5.1.1  Age and location of porphyry coppers

Most porphyry copper stocks were emplaced in late Mesozoic or in Tertiary times. Some, in island arcs, are as young as Pliocene. Palaeozoic and even Precambrian stocks are known, but they are rarer and often poorly mineralized. But not all younger stocks are viably mineralized; in Iran, only one in a group of ten Miocene stocks, Sar Cheshmeh, is worth mining. Figure 5.1 shows that most stocks follow the trends of subduction and collision zones, although there are some exceptions,

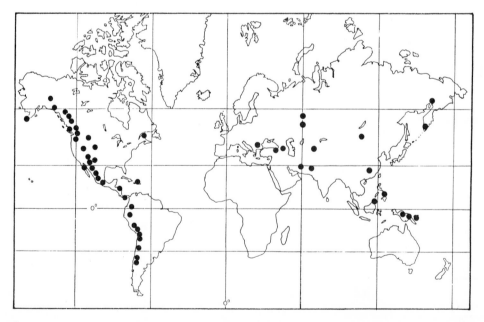

**Figure 5.1**  Porphyry copper and porphyry molybdenum areas of the world. The symbols refer to general areas where deposits occur, not to individual deposits. Note especially the relationship to plate edges.

notably in the western USA, which were probably associated with past underlying hot spots.

### 5.1.2 Origin of the metals

Porphyry copper stocks have an isotopic composition which relates them to I-granites generated during subduction from mantle wedge and oceanic crust (Fig. 5.2). These melted materials were fractionated, and the lighter felsic differentiates rose by their own buoyancy into continental crust to form granodioritic batholiths. Apophyses from the batholiths rose still further to form stocks only just below the surface and produced volcanic activity at the surface. But where did the copper come from?

The most obvious source of copper is from the subduction and melting of those copper-rich zones of sea floor described in Chapter 4. This copper would be incorporated into the granodiorites formed during partial melting of oceanic crust. But why the difference in by-products between continental porphyries and those in island arcs? Contamination by different crustal rocks the I-granites rose through may account for it, for the host rocks in the island arcs are predominantly volcanic as opposed to the more sedimentary successions of the continents. On the other hand, island arc porphyries are more dioritic than continental ones. So far, there is no answer.

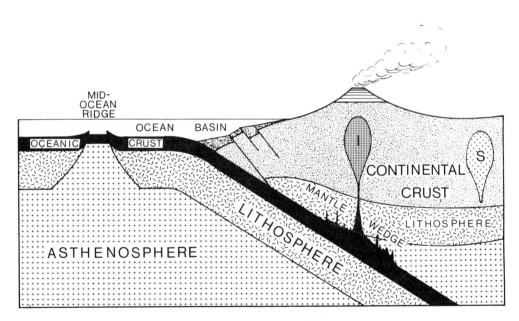

**Figure 5.2** A plate tectonic model for the formation of porphyry copper stocks. The isotopic ratios for $^{87}Sr:^{86}Sr$ and $^{34}S:^{32}S$ suggest that their parent I-granite batholiths (I) are developed from the fractionation of melted oceanic crust and mantle wedge, probably contaminated by continental crust. S-granites (S) related to many tin–silver and tin–tungsten deposits, are formed by anatexis of continental crust.

### 5.1.3 Mineralization and alteration

A porphyry copper stock is not consistently mineralized throughout. Viable ore may occur in only one of the rock types forming the composite stock, and even then there is a strong ore zoning. Superimposed on the stock and adjacent rocks are also several phases of alteration zoning. One is due to primary fluids within the consolidating stock magma, resulting in potash metasomatism and some silicification. This is overlapped and surrounded by a clay mineral and sericitic phyllic alteration and, further from the stock, a widespread propylitization in which carbonates, epidote, and chlorite abound; both are a result of meteoric water sinking through the intruded rocks, being heated, and rising again as part of a convection cell (Fig. 5.3). Stocks also exhibit a crackle texture of fine interlacing joints caused by resurgent boiling of fluids within the stock as pressures are relieved. All these factors have effects on the mineralization of the stock, especially the position of the copper sulphides.

Lowell and Guilbert (1970) developed what is now the generally-accepted model by synthesizing it from the common features of a number of American stocks. They envisaged a cylindrical copper-rich shell at the junction between the metasomatic potassic alteration zone and the zone of phyllic seritization and argillization. This copper-rich cylinder is enclosed by a copper-poor pyritic shell. Copper-rich is, however, only a relative term; the ore averages only about 0.5–0.7

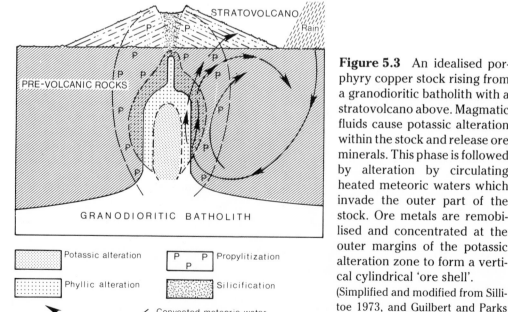

**Figure 5.3** An idealised porphyry copper stock rising from a granodioritic batholith with a stratovolcano above. Magmatic fluids cause potassic alteration within the stock and release ore minerals. This phase is followed by alteration by circulating heated meteoric waters which invade the outer part of the stock. Ore metals are remobilised and concentrated at the outer margins of the potassic alteration zone to form a vertical cylindrical 'ore shell'.
(Simplified and modified from Sillitoe 1973, and Guilbert and Parks 1986, and others)

per cent in most porphyries, sometimes less. Inside the copper-rich shell there is lower grade copper ore, and there may also be silicification; this part of the body may be richer in molybdenum. Sillitoe (1973) suggests that continental (or Andean) porphyry stocks underlie calc-alkaline sub-aerial stratovolcanoes (Fig. 5.3). In some regions, including the Andes, epithermal mineral deposits may be associated with these volcanic rocks.

Island-arc porphyries are less siliceous than those on continents and are often called the diorite model, although quartz diorite and diorite porphyries are not entirely unknown in continental areas. Diorite porphyries have a simpler zoning; they are richer in gold and poorer in molybdenum than the Lowell-Guilbert model. Colley (1976) even implies that undersea apophyses from such stocks are responsible for the volcanic activity which produces Kuroko deposits.

The copper sulphides in porphyry deposits include chalcopyrite, bornite, and sometimes the arsenical grey copper mineral, enargite ($Cu_3AsS_4$); molybdenum occurs as molybdenite ($MoS_2$). With such low grade deposits as these, secondary oxidation and sulphide enrichment can be very important to their economics and some deposits would not be worth working without it. At Sar Cheshmeh in Iran, the stock is leached to 50 m beneath the surface, leaving an average grade of under 0.2 per cent copper from a primary ore averaging a little under 1 per cent. There are no secondary oxides, but just below the watertable there are 350 million tonnes of secondary sulphide ore with 6 per cent copper at its top. Such secondary enrichment can make or break a deposit.

Only one porphyry copper deposit is known in Britain. It crops out as a dioritic apophysis from a deeper unexposed body near Dollgellau in Wales. Although no viable ore has been found, peat impregnated with copper leached from the deposit was mined in the last century as the Turf Copper Mine. The peat was burnt on site and the ash shipped for smelting. No gold has been reported, but the Dolgellau gold belt lies in the Harlech Dome immediately to the west.

Porphyry copper deposits supply more than half the world's copper. The Communist bloc is less fortunate in this type of ore than the west, but porphyries do occur in Bulgaria, the Urals, Caucasus, and further east, and again in China. Many Russian porphyries are Palaeozoic, one in Outer Mongolia is Precambrian.

### 5.1.4 Waste disposal

Low grade porphyry copper ores are mined in open pits on a massive scale; this results in hugh quantities of waste. Two hundred tonnes of ore must be mined to produce one tonne of copper from an 0.5 per cent copper ore, and 197 of those tonnes are discharged from the mill as fine-grained waste once the ore minerals have been extracted. In addition, over twice as much country rock overburden may have to be removed to reach the ore (Fig. 1.3); thus there may be 600 tonnes of waste to be disposed of to recover just one tonne of copper. To further complicate matters, broken ground occupies 30 per cent more space than when it was in place, so its bulk is greatly increased. Waste must be dumped where it will not cause hazards, for dumped tailings can liquify after rain and flow down valleys with devastating results. In 1985, tailings from the Prealpi Mineraria fluorite mine in northern Italy swept over the village of Stava and killed 250 people.

## 5.2  Contact metamorphic deposits and replacements

Ores may occur in carbonate rocks close to an acid or intermediate intrusion; very occasionally the mineralized rock is not a carbonate. This type of deposit has a number of names, but contact metamorphic and replacement deposit are at least descriptive. Other terms used include skarn, pyrometasomatic, and igneous metamorphic.

### 5.2.1  Contact deposits

Contact metamorphic deposits are usually small, with a few notable exceptions; they are also usually rich. Their ore mineralogy is relatively simple and falls into two main groups; oxide ores, such as magnetite, haematite, cassiterite, and the tungstate scheelite; and the sulphides, chalcopyrite, bornite, silver-rich galena, black iron-bearing sphalerite, molybdenite, and abundant pyrite. The oxide ores are found close to the igneous contact; the sulphides further away. The mineralogy of the gangue minerals, which form part of the contact metamorphic aureole, is more complex.

When a carbonate rock is intruded, a metamorphic aureole is developed which decreases in intensity with distance from the contact. The aureole may be metres to many tens of metres wide. Close to the igneous rock there is complete recrystallization of the carbonate with calc-silicate minerals developed by the introduction of siliceous fluids from the intrusion. Notable new minerals are the amphiboles tremolite-actinolite; the pyroxenes diopside-hedenbergite; and epidote, wollastonite and the lime garnets, grossular and andradite. Quartz and opaline silica may also be deposited and, if the original carbonate was dolomitic, serpentine may occur. Such altered rocks are called skarns, Swedish for rubbish, a term originally used for the stone ruined by intrusive dykes in marble quarries. Tactite, from contactite, is an alternative term used in the USA.

Although there is a decrease in metamorphism away from the intrusion there is often a culmination of garnet some distance from the contact which may form a massive, heavy, granular garnet rock. This garnet zone divides oxide ores, which are close to the contact, from sulphides on its far side (Fig. 5.4a). Figure 5.4b is a miniature contact metamorphic deposit in Iran, formed where a narrow feldspar porphyry sill has intruded dolomite. The ore is haematite and it still shows relict bedding. Small veinlets of ore penetrate the porphyry near its contact; of particular interest are the complete lack of mineralization at the lower contact and the absence of ore east of the fault. Mineralization was post-faulting, therefore at least a little later than consolidation of the intrusion.

Iron Mountain in Utah, USA, is a contrast in size (Fig. 5.5). There, huge magnetite ore bodies follow the contact of the carbonate Homestake Formation around an oval quartz monzonite laccolith 8 km long. Two similarly sized deposits lie immediately to the north.

(a)

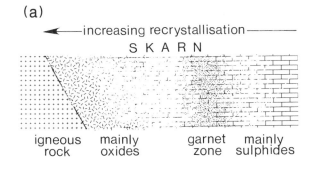

(b)

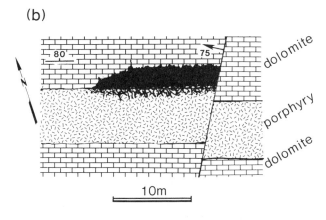

**Figure 5.4**

(a) An ideal cross-section through an igneous metamorphic deposit in carbonate rock. The carbonate has been recrystallized and new minerals introduced to form skarn. Oxide ore minerals occur mainly between the garnet zone and the igneous contact; sulphides are found mainly on the other side of the garnet zone.

(b) A miniature igneous metamorphic ore body found in Iran. A 7 m wide white feldspar porphyry sill intruded dolomite to form a haematite ore body 2 m thick and 16 m long in the hangingwall. Ore is massive with relict bedding; there is some veining in the porphyry; skarn is poorly developed. Ore does not cross the fault or occur on the footwall.

**Figure 5.5** Lion Pit, Iron Mountain, S-W Utah, USA. The grey Homestake (limestone) Formation lies above a laccolith of quartz monzonite about 8 km across. The photo shows monzonite on the left, massive magnetite in the centre, and garnet rock to the right.

### 5.2.2 Origin

It is generally assumed that contact deposits are formed by fluids emanating from the intruding rock shortly after intrusion and following the development of skarn. Skarnification appears to be a conditioning of the rock prior to mineralization. The fluids are siliceous aqueous differentiates which remain after consolidation of the magma and penetrate the invaded rocks during shrinkage as temperature fall. At Iron Mountain, biotites adjacent to deeply-penetrating joints in the monzonite have been bleached by loss of iron, suggesting that in this case fluids had leached iron from rock minerals which had already crystallized. Boyle (1968; 1979), however, has presented evidence that in some ore deposits metals may have moved from the metamorphosed sedimentary rocks inwards towards the igneous contact, possibly by ionic diffusion through pore waters, or by movement of interstitial water itself attempting to equilibrate the difference between the dry intrusive and the wetter cooler rocks outside it.

Contact metamorphic deposits are common in many areas where there are small intrusive bodies such as dykes, sills, laccoliths, pipes and stocks. They are also associated with porphyry copper stocks.

### 5.2.3 Other replacements

Ore deposits, notably of lead and zinc sulphides, sometimes occur at a considerable distance from an igneous body, but are obviously related to it. Many ore deposits in carbonate rocks several kilometres from porphyry copper stocks fall into this class. Some fit into the class of igneous metamorphic deposits used as a blanket term by Park and MacDiarmid (1964, p. 250), but the amount of metamorphism in some of these replacements is minimal.

## 5.3 Veins, lodes and reefs

A vein is a tabular or flat lenticular epigenetic body composed largely of quartz, carbonates, or occasionally sulphates, sulphides or other minerals. 'Lode' is an archaic synonym, 'reef' is a vague colloquial word used to cover anything from an epigenetic vein to a syngenetic gold-bearing conglomerate. Avoid both terms whenever possible.

Veins usually have well-defined walls, although some include intensely altered wall rocks, such as greisen. Quartz and carbonate make up the bulk of most veins, but topaz, tourmaline, muscovite, chlorite, microcline, adularia, garnet, fluorite, barite, and rarer minerals may be present too. The carbonates are calcite, dolomite or ankerite $(Ca(Fe,Mg)(CO_3)_2)$ and, in low temperature veins, cryptocrystalline and opaline silica can also occur. Some veins may be composed mainly of barite, fluorite or even pyrite. Internal structures range from a single generation of white massive 'bull' quartz to several generations of quartz, carbonate, and other minerals. Some veins are fissure fillings, others are mineralized breccias, or even silicified shear zones; low-temperature veins may show large crystals growing from the walls, occasionally leaving empty vughs or geodes into which well-terminated quartz or calcite crystals project.

Veins may be vertical, dipping, or horizontal, or even follow folded structures. Their walls may be parallel or pinch and swell. They can be any size; the Comstock Lode of Nevada was 6 km long and up to 300 m wide; most are much smaller. They may occur singly or in swarms of sub-parallel veins such as the Mother Lode of California, where an *en echelon* succession of lenticular veins strikes northwards for 200 km; or they may form a huge intersecting stockwork of variously sized veins as at Butte in Montana. Vein composition is temperature-dependent, and temperature forms the broad base for classification.

### 5.3.1  Vein temperatures

Veins associated with igneous activity can be classified into three temperature groups.

Epithermal veins formed at < 300°C
Mesothermal veins formed from 240°C to 400°C
Hypothermal veins formed at > 400°C

Temperatures between groups overlap because their differences depend also on their geological associations and the sources of their ore-bearing fluids. Their mineral compositions differ too, and that is how the groups are recognised, Table 5.1, lists a number of mineral geothermometers.

**Table 5.1**  Mineral geothermometers showing their temperature ranges.

|  | *Hypothermal* | *Mesothermal* | *Epithermal* |
|---|---|---|---|
| Ore minerals | Gold<br>Cassiterite<br>Wolfram<br>Bismuthinite | Gold<br>Chalcopyrite<br>Bornite<br>Molybdenite<br>Grey coppers<br>Galena (with silver)<br>Sphalerite | Gold<br>Acanthite<br>Ruby silvers<br>Cinnabar<br>Stibnite<br>Galena (with silver)<br>Sphalerite<br>Realgar and orpiment |
| Gangues | Pyrrhotite<br>Arsenopyrite<br>Magnetite<br>Specular haematite<br>Garnet<br>Topaz<br>Tourmaline<br>Pyroxene<br>Amphibole<br>Quartz | Pyrrhotite<br>(Arsenopyrite)<br><br><br><br><br><br><br><br>Quartz | Marcasite<br>Siderite<br>Rhodochrosite<br>Other carbonates<br>Adularia<br><br><br><br><br>Quartz and<br>chalcedony |

Pyrite is ubiquitous. Two or more minerals are needed to establish a vein type. This table is not exclusive; other minerals can occur but are rarer, or not confined to any vein type.

Gold and pyrite occur in all groups, but most minerals are more restricted in their temperature ranges. Ore fluids cool while migrating from their sources, so that minerals in the lower part of a vein system may not always be identical with those found higher up. The sources themselves also cool, producing cooler fluids, so later minerals may differ from those deposited earlier in the system.

Taken generally, hypothermal veins are associated with plutonic rocks and were formed at some depth; mesothermal veins are related to shallower intrusions; epithermal veins are associated with volcanic activity. However, as in all geology, not everything fits into neat categories and not every vein fits into a neat thermal classification.

### 5.3.2 Hypothermal veins

The principal ore minerals found in hypothermal veins are cassiterite ($SnO_2$), wolfram (($Fe,Mn)WO_4$) and native gold. Hypothermal veins are commonly associated with granites, notably with cupolas rising from underlying S-type batholiths of anatectic granites (Fig. 5.2). Veins occur in the upper parts of the cupolas and in the surrounding regionally-metamorphosed rocks in which such granites occur. Figure 5.6 shows an idealized cross-section through a Cornish-type cupola. Granite has intruded the soft Devonian slates, which the Cornish call killas, and a hood of early consolidated granite has solidified outside a still liquid

**Figure 5.6** Diagrammatic section through a cupola (such as a Cornish granite) formed above a batholith. The granite (G) intrudes the slates (S), and quartz porphyry dykes (hatched) penetrate the surrounding rocks. A hood of rapidly-consolidating granite (H) forms a thick skin around the still-mobile magma, and an aqueous, volatile-rich, siliceous fluid (F) accumulates beneath it. As the granite core solidifies and the mass shrinks, this fluid is released along conjugate fractures and precipitates as veins (black). Some veins follow dyke margins (W) as at Wheal Jane; others intersect, with ore enrichment at their junctions. In Cornwall, veins in granite and close to it carry tin; further away they contain copper, a result of temperature zoning.

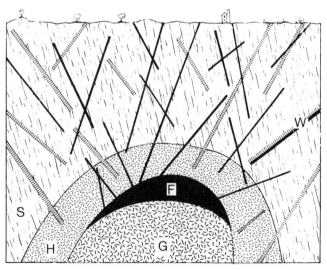

core. Quartz porphyry and microgranite dykes, called elvans in Cornwall, have invaded the hood and surrounding rocks along fissures and faults resulting from granite intrusion. Aqueous siliceous fluid has accumulated at the top of the granite as it consolidated beneath the granite hood, a fluid rich in volatiles such as boron and fluorine, and containing tin, tungsten, base metals, iron, arsenic, and sulphur. As the cupola core consolidates, stresses in the hood and killas create a conjugate fracture system along which this fluid escapes and precipitates its mineral matter. Tin is deposited within the hood and the nearest killas; copper is deposited mainly in the killas but overlaps tin mineralization. Gangues are predominantly quartz, with fluorite and accessory topaz, tourmaline, chlorite, and even microcline, plus pyrite and arsenopyrite (FeAsS). Later veins carry zinc and lead sulphides further afield. Tungsten post-dates tin and pre-dates copper. Granite wall-rocks are hydrothermally altered during vein formation to a greisen selvage of muscovite and granular quartz; walls in the killas contain garnet and axinite.

Cornwall (with Devon) has long been considered to contain within its boundaries classic examples of mineral zoning caused by temperature. Tin occurs close to the granite, grading into a copper mineralization outside the granite, followed by a silver-rich zinc-lead zone. Further still from the granite, iron and antimony sometimes occur. Thus we appear to have mineral zones which cover most of the hypothermal and mesothermal ranges, if not more.

Many in the past have held that hypothermal veins were formed at such depth that they could not normally show a temperature zoning because the intruded rocks were almost as hot as the mineralizing fluids. They used a number of 'typical' hypothermal gold deposits to illustrate this. They included the Homestake Mine of South Dakota, USA; Broken Hill in New South Wales, Australia; Morrho Velho in Brazil; and Champion Reef in the Kolar goldfield of India, as examples where ore was of one consistent type over vertical ranges of 3000–4000 m. Recently, it has been shown tht the first three examples are not in fact epigenetic but are most probably strongly-deformed and metamorphosed syngenetic deposits associated with hot springs. Champion Reef is the only 'typical hypothermal' deposit which survives the group. This is a quartz vein which strikes for 7 km conformably with its Precambrian schist host rocks, dipping at 55° at the surface and steepening to vertical at the mining limit of over 3000 m. Gold occurs in a number of rich ore shoots, but the vein does not otherwise change in character over its whole lateral or vertical extent. Ore is related to a nearby granite originally intruded at considerable depth into metamorphic country rocks. Here there is no zoning and ore fluids may well have matched the country rocks in temperature. The zoning in Devon and Cornwall, however, suggests that there the granites were much shallower and the country rocks were cooler away from the immediate granite aureole.

### 5.3.3 Mesothermal veins

Mesothermal ores are major producers of the base metals copper, lead, and zinc. Veins formed at these temperatures are commonly associated with granitic to dioritic intrusions, although not necessarily connected with them. The ore fluids are, in many instances, formed from meteoric water and only sometimes mixed with juvenile fluids from the intrusions themselves.

A most interesting discovery was made in the early 1960s when a well was sunk to 1.6 km in the Salton Sea of southern Caifornia to investigate hot spring waters for geothermal energy. The well passed only through sedimentary rocks and reached 300° to 370°C at its bottom, where it tapped a saline fluid which precipitated five to eight tonnes of siliceous scale in the surface plant, containing 20 per cent copper and 2 per cent silver, over a period of three months. Oxygen and deuterium isotopes showed the fluid to be derived from meteoric water, and it carried 25 per cent chlorides, 540 ppm zinc, 102 ppm lead, 8 ppm copper, but only 18 ppm sulphur. Rain water had penetrated to great depth, where it had been heated by a presumed intrusion below and leached mineral matter from the rocks it passed through. If this fluid had encountered a source of sulphur, it would have presumably shed its base metals as sulphides in suitable fractures at temperatures within the mesothermal range.

Boyle (1968; 1979) has suggested a somewhat similar mechanism for cobalt-silver deposits in Ontario, Canada, and at Joachimsthal in Czechoslovakia; he points out that the mineralization is similar in both places but that in Ontario the igneous rock is diabase (i.e. dolerite) and at Joachimsthal a granite. He considers that the igneous rocks were merely sources of energy which moved the ore fluids although, in his thesis, the fluids were connate waters and pore fluids. Not only are his metals derived from the surrounding rocks, but the sulphur is too, and these materials were sucked into shear zones to form mineral veins.

Not all mesothermal veins are related directly, or even indirectly, to meteoric or connate waters. Some are closely related to intrusions, as are the zinc-lead veins in Devon and Cornwall, UK. Others, such as the gold ores of Canada, the Mother Lode of California, USA, and the source rocks of the gold which went to form the fossil placers of South Africa, owe their origin to the metamorphism of gold-bearing greenstones by nearby intrusions, although pore waters again probably played a part. As stated earlier, not everything can be neatly packaged in geology.

### 5.3.4 Epithermal veins

Many famous precious metal mines are epithermal, among them the great

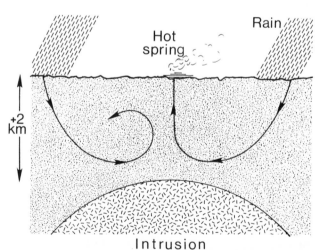

**Figure 5.7**
A theoretical cross-section to show the course of convected meteoric water, i.e. rain water, which has penetrated a sequence of sedimentary rocks to a considerable depth. Some fluid may reach the surface as hot springs, having lost most of its metal content. Some may never return to the surface.

Comstock Lode of Nevada and the *bonanzas* of Cripple Creek in Colorado, USA, Pachuca in Mexico, and Hauraki in New Zealand. The ores are silver-rich gold ores or gold-rich silver ores: they carry native gold; electrum, a natural gold alloy containing up to 36 per cent silver; gold tellurides and even selenides; acanthite, the low-temperature form of silver sulphide; and the silver sulpharsenides and sulphantimonides called ruby silvers. In addition, the veins may contain stibnite, cinnabar, realgar, orpiment, and even some sphalerite and silver-rich galena. Copper may also occur, usually as the copper sulpharsenide 'grey copper' mineral, enargite. Sometimes the ore may be in a massive quartz vein several kilometres long and tens of metres wide, as at Comstock; more commonly, epigenetic precious metals occur in stockworks or breccia zones. Country rocks are andesitic to rhyolitic lavas and tuffs. They have been extensively propylitized, that is, they have been altered to chloritic rocks containing epidote, calcite, and pyrite.

The ores have been deposited from solutions whose sources are meteoric waters which have been heated within the country rocks and returned to the surface where they have formed siliceous hot springs. Fluids probably sank to several kilometres before rising. Within 1 km of the surface, the ore fluids fell to below their critical pressure and boiled, precipitating at least part of their metallic load. Boiling is also probably responsible for much of the brecciation found in this type of deposit. Some geologists consider that resurgent boiling causes hydraulic brecciation and is a significant mechanism in forming pathways for ore solutions (Phillips 1972; 1986).

Because ore deposition has occured in the boiling zone, many epithermal precious metal deposits have limited vertical extents to their mineable mineralization, sometimes as little as 100 m. However, in many deposits, boiling probably occurred many times and at different elevations in the vein system, spreading the ore zone over greater vertical ranges. Temperatures in many cases were as much as 300°C, but ores were also deposited at much lesser temperature, possibly as low as 50°C in some fields. Low-temperature veins may even show open-spacing filling, crustified and colloform textures, and banding of successive generations of vein material. Quartz, calcite, barite, adularia and opaline silica are common gangue minerals. Epithermal gold veins are notoriously erratic and are sometimes called *bonanzas*, Spanish for 'good luck', for each very rich pocket may be separated from the next by large distances of barren vein. But not all epithermal veins carry precious metals.

Mercury and antimony veins are also commonly epithermal. In many instances, there is a close volcanic connection. The Sizma-Ladik mercury field of central Turkey, which was first mined over 8000 years ago (Barnes & Bailey 1972), lies several kilometres away from the nearest exposures of volcanic rocks, although dacitic dykes occur nearby and are almost certainly related to the ore. Further to the SE at Niğde, however, mercury and antimony ores occur on the edge of an extensive volcanic field which stretches as far as Mount Ararat, a thousand kilometres to the east. The veins at Ladik are carbonate with some quartz, barite, fluorite, and cinnabar, with traces of stibnite and the copper sulphantimonide, tetrahedrite. At Niğde thé vein is mainly quartz but contains both cinnabar and stibnite, not a happy mixture for they are difficult to separate for sale.

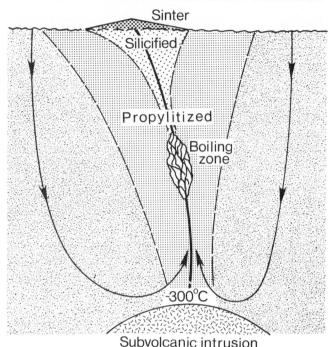

Sinter

Silicified

Propylitized

Boiling zone

-300°C

Subvolcanic intrusion

**Figure 5.8**
An idealized epithermal pre-cious metal vein. Meteoric water sinks through the vol-canic and sedimentary rocks and is heated by an underlying subvolcanic intrusion. The heated water leaches mineral matter and rises up a con-venient fissure to about 1 km below the surface, where it boils, hydraulically fractures the adjacent rock, and deposits part of its mineral content. Cooling water passes upwards, silicifying the adjacent rocks and forming sinters at the surface. There is widespread propylitization.

### 5.3.5 Fluids at depth

Russian broadcasts have recently reported that a well sunk in the Kola peninsula for scientific reasons has encountered a zone of abundant mineralized water 4.5 to 9 km deep in rocks fractured and disaggregated by very high pressures, which gives them a relatively high porosity. There is no indication of the isotopic composition of the water. Copper, nickel, cobalt and zinc sulphides are also reported in the hole. Is the water released from the rocks by metamorphism, or is it part of the immense quantity of water subducted within ocean floor rocks, estimated as equal to all the oceans every 500 million years, and never accounted for?

## 5.4 Pegmatites

'Simple' pegmatites are coarse-grained veins or dykes, usually of granitic composi-tion and usually found in or close to granitoid rocks. Economically they can be sources of feldspar and muscovite mica, but little else. Some syenitic varieties may contain corundum, even sapphire and ruby. Here, we are more concerned with 'complex' pegmatites.

Complex pegmatites are the source of a variety of rarer minerals and elements. At one time, before the discovery of the Spor Mountain ores (section 4.6), they were the only source of beryllium. They also produce niobium, tantalum, caesium, lithium, rare earths, and a little tin. Complex pegmatites are usually small ore bodies some tens of metres long with low individual productions, although a very few are much larger. They commonly occur in groups.

### 5.4.1 Occurrence

Complex pegmatites have a generally granitic bulk composition and are distinguished by an internal zoning of different textures and compositions. Their form may be dyke-like, pipe-like, ovoid, or even completely irregular. They can be quite unpredictable, pinch and swell, suddenly expand into a wide body, or cut out entirely. Some in East Africa appear to have been emplaced largely by replacement of the country rocks, for biotitized schist wall rock caught up in pegmatite passes into biotitized schlieren and biotite-rich ghosts, yet maintains the same foliation direction as the surrounding mica schists. Pegmatites may also reflect the composition of their host rocks; in microcline granite gneisses they may be potash-rich, in mica schists, mica-rich, and in quartzite have a huge quartz core.

### 5.4.2 Zoning

Complex pegmatites have a distinctive textural and compositional zoning, as shown in Figure 5.9 and below.

| | |
|---|---|
| Border zone (no ore) | A discontinuous rim of coarse granitic texture and composition, a few centimetres wide. |
| Wall zone (poor ore) | Microcline pegmatite or graphic granite, often rich in black tourmaline (schorl). |
| Intermediate zone (main ore zone) | Zone of very large crystals of microcline, albite, quartz and micas; some crystals measured in metres. Albite may occur as sheaves of replacement cleavelandite (Fig. 5.10). Muscovite is unusable owing to distortion and defects. Lithium minerals occur, especially lepidolite $[K(Li,Al)_3(Si,Al)_4O_{10}(F,OH)_2]$. Beryl $[Be_3Al_2Si_6O_{18}]$ may be in crystal aggregates weighing up to a tonne. Columbite-tantalite $[(Fe,Mn)(Nb,Ta)_2O_6]$ can be present in all zones, but rich pockets tend to follow the quartz core margin. Cassiterite $[SnO_2]$, pollucite $[2CsO_2.2Al_2O_3.9SiO_2.H_2O]$ and other ore minerals may occur including those of yttrium, cerium, and other lanthanides. Uranium and thorium are only present in forms unacceptable to industry e.g. samarskite (2.2.2). |
| Quartz core (barren) | Massive milky white bull quartz. |

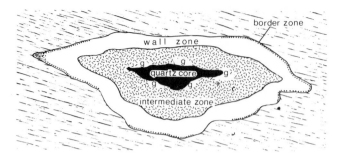

**Figure 5.9**
Zoning in a complex pegmatite. The quartz core lies within the intermediate zone, with lenses of greisen (g) at its margin. The wall zone surrounds the intermediate zone, and a discontinuous border zone marks the pegmatite boundary. Most ore minerals occur in the intermediate zone.

### 5.4.3 Origin

Opinions on the origin of pegmatites differ. They range from a fluid supply of continually changing composition reacting with previously-formed minerals deposited in an open system to produce successive replacements of one mineral by another; to the other extreme of a bubble of volatile-rich granitoid fluid crystallizing entirely in its own closed system, with the rest fluid changing in composition as

**Figure 5.10**
Part of a complex pegmatite exposed in a prospecting pit in central Uganda. The microcline is part of a single crystal of pale greenish amazonstone; cleavelandite occurs as coarse white sheaves; thick books and rosettes of zinnwaldite (a lithium-bearing biotite) occur at the microcline and quartz margins; the topaz is a granular, fine-grained non-gem form. The clay gouge splitting the massive quartz is an unexplained problem. Note the extraordinarily coarse texture of this body, which also contains some beryl.

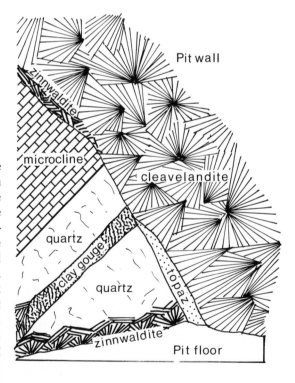

it precipitates minerals and then, through disequilibrium, reacting with the minerals it has previously deposited. Both theories explain a relatively regular zoning from the walls inwards, and both require a volatile-enriched fluid derived from a consolidating granitic magma. However, field observation indicates that, in some pegmatite fields at least, considerable amounts of country rock are replaced which influence the final pegmatite composition. In fact, in such cases, the amount of volatile material required from outside to effect the conversion of country rock to pegmatite is minimal.

Pegmatites occur within granites and granitic gneisses, and in the regionally-metamorphosed rocks surrounding them. Mineralization is related to position. Those in granite tend to be beryl-bearing, those just outside the granite carry niobium or tantalum, those further from the granite may contain tin.

## 5.5 Magmatic segregation of sulphides

Some silicate magmas can hold up to 10 per cent metallic sulphides in solution. As the magmas cool, metallic sulphides are shed from the silicate melt as immiscible droplets. These droplets sink through the much lighter silicate melt, coalescing when they meet each other to form larger drops, and eventually collect at the bottom of the silicate magma as a matte, a term used by metallurgists to describe fluid metallic sulphides produced during smelting. The huge basin-like nickel-copper-bearing body at Sudbury in Ontario, Canada, has traditionally been taken as an example of segregation, although radical differences of opinion have developed recently regarding details of the process. Direct magmatic segregation is still the accepted origin for nickel ores elsewhere, none of which compare in size with Sudbury.

### 5.5.1 The Sudbury ores

The huge Sudbury nickel-copper sulphide deposits were discovered in a Canadian Pacific Railway cutting in the later part of the last century. The discovery was looked upon as a copper deposit with the nickel ores an inconvenience, until it was found that a cupro-nickel alloy, monel metal, could be made directly from the ore; this alloy is particularly resistant to marine corrosion. Later still, Sudbury became primarily a nickel producer, and copper was looked on merely as a by-product.

The general geology at Sudbury is shown in Figure 5.11. There is a basin-shaped feature 60 km long by 27 km wide which contains a sill-like igneous body 1.5 km thick. The intrusion is sandwiched between the Lower Huronian (2000 Ma) Whitewater Series of sandstones, shales, carbonates and (Onaping) volcani-clastic rocks above; and Lower Huronian greenstones and sedimentary rocks, and Keewatin gneisses (2600 Ma) which form the basement, below. Intrusive granites also occur. The intrusion was assumed to have been emplaced beneath the Whitewater Series as a giant horizontal sill before sagging to its present synclinal form as a result of the withdrawal of magma from below. The intrusion is complex. Originally intermediate in composition, the magma segregated to produce a granophyric upper part to the sill. Below the granophyre is gabbro

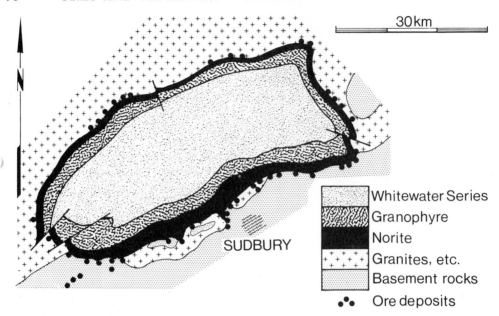

**Figure 5.11**  Simplified geology of the Sudbury region, Ontario, Canada. (Various sources)

which passes downwards into a felsic norite (15 per cent hypersthene). Close to the sill base the norite becomes increasingly mafic, with over 50 per cent hypersthene. The sulphides occur in a noritic sub-layer lying between the basement rocks and the mafic norite. This sub-layer is partly concentrated in depressions in the basement topography. The problem has always been, where and when did segregation occur?

The ore is massive pyrrhotite with copper mainly as chalcopyrite and the nickel as pentlandite $[(Ni,Fe)_9S_8]$. Small but valuable amounts of platinum sulphides and arsenides also occur. The general tenor of the ore is about 1 per cent nickel and 1 per cent copper, but nickel has more than two and a half times the value of copper.

### 5.5.2  Origin of the Sudbury ores

Hypotheses on the origin of the Sudbury complex have gone through several stages. The earliest postulate a horizontal sill of intermediate magma intruded beneath the Whitewater Series, which then differentiated in place. The granitic fraction formed the upper granophyre and the more mafic differentiate produced the gabbro-norites below; the sulphides sank to the base, concentrating especially in the lows of the basal surface. Problems arose with this hypothesis, the sublayer being only one of them, and it was then suggested that there was an initial differentiation into a granitic and a gabbroic-noritic magma in the magma chamber. This gave the hypothesis that the gabbro-norite was intruded first and differentiated into the fractions now seen; the granophyre was intruded later. The noritic sub-layer represented the residual dregs of the magma chamber, injected late with the sulphides along the floor of basement rocks below the norites. A

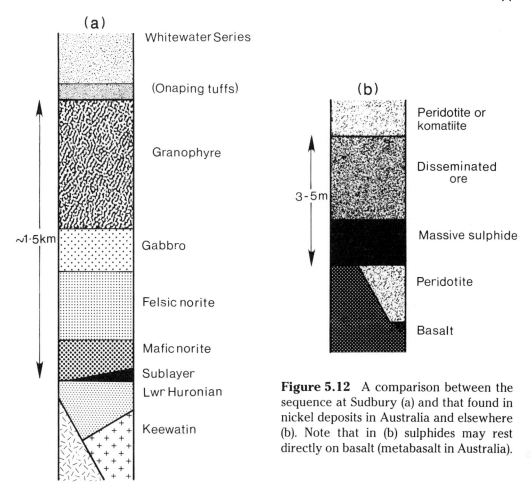

**Figure 5.12** A comparison between the sequence at Sudbury (a) and that found in nickel deposits in Australia and elsewhere (b). Note that in (b) sulphides may rest directly on basalt (metabasalt in Australia).

theory of partial differentiation in the magma chamber and three intrusive phases does not explain many of the features found at Sudbury. Even the existence of the giant sill is improbable; Dietz had another explanation.

### 5.5.3 Astroblemes

Dietz (1964) suggested that Sudbury resulted from the impact of a huge nickel-iron meteorite which he called an astrobleme, Greek for 'star-wound'. The meteorite struck the Lower Huronian and Keewatin rocks about 1700 million years ago to produce a crater about 50 km across and 2 km deep. The nickel-iron meteorite liquefied on impact and was splattered over the crater floor and walls. The heat of impact melted the rocks deep below the crater, which welled up to form an extrusive lopolith in the floor of the crater, covered by the fall-back material from the impact (which is now seen as the Onaping tuff and breccia lying on top of the granophyre). The melted rock differentiated in place to give the sequence now seen of granophyre, gabbro, norite, ore. The crater was later filled with sediments which now form the rest of the Whitewater Series (Fig. 5.13). Finally, the

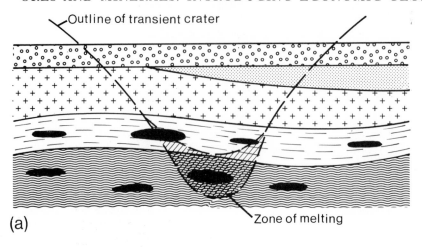

(a)

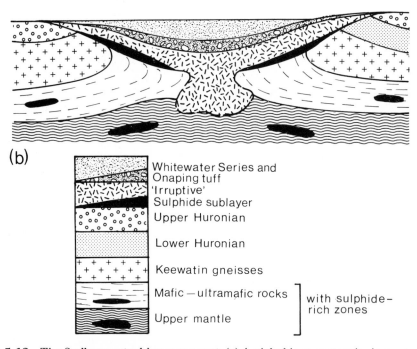

(b)

| | |
|---|---|
| | Whitewater Series and Onaping tuff |
| | 'Irruptive' |
| | Sulphide sublayer |
| | Upper Huronian |
| | Lower Huronian |
| | Keewatin gneisses |
| | Mafic – ultramafic rocks |
| | Upper mantle |

with sulphide-rich zones

**Figure 5.13**  The Sudbury astrobleme concept. (a) A nickel-iron meteorite impact causes a vast transient crater, and melts the rocks below; elastic rebound reduces the crater depth, and the remaining hollow is partially filled with airborne debris, now seen as the Onaping tuff. (b) Melted rock intrudes beneath the tuff as an extrusive lopolith and differentiates in place; the sub-layer is injected at the base of the intrusion. Ore is formed partly from melted meteorite and partly from copper-iron sulphide zones in the rocks melted. Finally, the Whitewater Series filled what remained of the depression.
(Adapted from Pattison 1979)

Grenville orogeny thrust north-westwards to compress the crater into its present elongate shape (Fig. 5.11). These ideas have since been refined. The copper was derived from the melting of rocks already rich in sulphides, and Pattison (1979) concludes there was general magmatic differentiation with segregation of the sulphides, which were later injected along the footwall.

The astrobleme concept explains many inconsistencies of the earlier ideas. The extensive brecciation and shatter cones found in the old rocks can now be accounted for. NASA (National Aeronautics and Space Administration) was quickly convinced of the astrobleme theory and sent its astronauts to Sudbury to examine the shatter cones so that they could recognize impact effects when they reached the moon. Most, but not all, Sudbury geologists are also convinced. Guilbert and Parks (1986, p. 328) remark there is no middle ground, you either believe in astroblemes or you do not; yet there is common ground in that both extremes require segregation from a magma. The difference of opinion is in how the magma is generated.

### 5.5.4 Other nickel deposits

Sudbury is by far the largest single nickel deposit in the world, but nickel also occurs elsewhere and in deposits where there is little doubt that the sulphides have been concentrated primarily by segregation of magmatic rocks in place without the help of astroblemes. One of the newcomers to nickel mining is the old goldfield in Western Australia, once famed for the Golden Mile at Kalgoorlie. There the ore is associated with komatiite lavas and sills in Archaean greenstones of the Yilgarn block. The sulphides are mainly concentrated in depressions on the upper surface of the footwall metabasalts and have undoubtedly segregated from the overlying komatiite lavas and sill-like dunite intrusions. Ore may be massive or banded, with stockworks and disseminated sulphides above. There is some controversy over the details of segregation; some suggest that the banded ore is a result of metamorphism, others that the massive ore is formed by remobilization of sulphides during metamorphism. Nickel orefields elsewhere have similar characteristics, and these komatiite-associated ores are compared with those at Sudbury in Figure 5.12. Size is one obvious difference and there are also great differences in the host rocks. But also, copper equals nickel in amount at Sudbury but is only a minor constituent in komatiite related deposits. Platinum is a useful by-product only where copper is abundant. In komatiite deposits, platinum is almost absent although nickel grade is generally better, at about 2 per cent.

## 5.6 Chromium deposits

Chrome ores have a close affinity with ultramafic rocks. They occur as segregations in either layered intrusions such as the Bushveld Complex, South Africa, which contains an estimated 87 per cent of all the world's potential chromium reserves (*World Mining Equipment*, August 1986), or in podiform deposits in ophiolites within alpine chains. The main producers are South Africa and Zimbabwe, USSR, Albania, the Philippines and Turkey. Smaller amounts come from Greece, Cyprus, Cuba, Pakistan, and Iran.

### 5.6.1 Chromite ores

The only commercial ore mineral is chromite ($FeO.Cr_2O_3$), a spinel. It is a low-value commodity which must normally form nearly 100 per cent of the ore in the ground to be economically recoverable, as beneficiation of the ore is usually either uneconomic or impracticable. To be saleable as metallurgical grade, chromite must have a chrome to iron ratio of better than 2.5:1, and consist of 70 per cent lump ore in pieces of over 15 cm in size. These specifications reduce large quantities of potential metallurgical ore to chemical or refractory grades. Recently, however, specifications for metallurgical ore have been relaxed, greatly to the benefit of South Africa which cannot meet the 2.5:1 ratio. New chromium plasma-arc technology will also soon make pelletized or even finely-milled ore acceptable (*ibid*). Lower grade ores are used for the production of chromic acid for plating and for refractory furnace linings. In general the higher quality chrome ore occurs in podiform deposits, and we will confine ourselves to this type of deposit here.

### 5.6.2 Alpine podiform deposits

Chromite deposits occur as clusters of massive chromite lenses in the ophiolitic rocks of alpine chains, notably in the Urals, Albania, Turkey and the Philippines. Individual lenses are usually less than 1.5 million tonnes of ore in size and less than 100 m long, although bodies of up to 90 million tonnes occur in the Urals. These deposits are called podiform because they tend to form fat lenses; vein-like lenses which pinch and swell for a kilometre or more do also occur, and some bodies are folded or otherwise disturbed. Ore margins may show polished slickensided surfaces; elsewhere, massive chromite may pass into nodular material called leopard or grape shot ore, with ovoid pellets of chromite surrounded by interstitial serpentinized dunite. Alternatively, nodules may be of serpentinized dunite

**Figure 5.14**
Leopard ore. Chromite nodules in dunite; the nodules are about 1 cm long and distinctly show serpentine-filled 'pull-apart' fractures.

surrounded by chromite. Such textures are presumed to result from liquid-liquid unmixing (Fig. 5.14).

### 5.6.3 Origin of podiform chromite

There can be few deposits which have had so many and such varied origins attributed to them as podiform chrome ores. In the past, most chromite geologists agreed that chrome ores showed evidence of movement after solidification, and that the pods had been squeezed into position from considerable depths, but from where, and just when segregation and consolidation of the ore mineral and its enclosing dunite occurred was a matter for great speculation. As with so many geological enigmas, the breakthrough came with the development of plate tectonics.

Recent ideas (Cann 1981) suggest that the process commences in the asthenosphere below a (back arc) spreading centre. As the asthenosphere rises to fill the space between two lithospheric plates moving apart, globules of magma separate from the partially molten asthenosphere and begin to rise. They meet the other globules to become larger and larger as they rise. The residual harzburgite forms part of the accreting lithospheric plate while the magma bodies rise and fractionate to form basaltic bubbles towing olivine-rich dunitic tails, which eventually part company from them (Fig. 5.15). The bubbles continue upwards

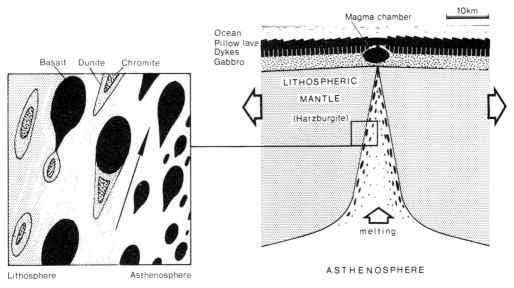

**Figure 5.15** The formation of podiform chromite lenses below a sea-floor spreading centre. Partially melted asthenosphere sheds small globules of basaltic magma; globules coalesce as they rise to form larger and larger bodies but, as pressure decreases, the basalt becomes oversaturated in olivine; excess olivine separates from the basalt as a tail, taking chromite with it. Tails eventually detach to form chromite pods surrounded by dunite within the basalt-depleted asthenosphere, i.e. harzburgite. The basalt magma rises to feed the magma chamber.
(Adapted from Cann 1981)

to feed the magma chamber below the spreading centre, the tails segregate into dunite lenses with chromite cores, stranded within the residual harzburgite which goes to form the lithospheric mantle. The harzburgite, with its dunite-chromite lenses, is pushed sideways towards the destructive plate margins where it may, or may not, be eventually obducted onto continental rocks as a chromite-bearing ophiolite zone.

This hypothesis explains many of the features observed in chromite-bearing ophiolite zones. The country rock (usually serpentinized) is harzburgite underlying gabbros. The chromite occurs in serpentinized dunite lenses and shows tiny sub-parallel 'pull-apart' fractures filled with serpentized dunite in nodular parts of the ore, indicating movement after the chromite had solidified (Fig. 5.16a). The nodular textures indicate the unmixing of the chromite and dunite fluids 'frozen' during segregation; other textures in minor bands within dunite show cumulate settling, such as the 'frilled tops' to some thin chromite bands in dunite (Fig. 16b). These bands show that not all chromite in the dunite pods segregates into large bodies. There are also many 1–3 m long by 5–10 cm wide bands of chromite found in both dunite and the enclosing harzburgite.

### 5.6.4 Conclusions

The history of hypotheses of chromite deposits is one illustration of the importance of plate tectonics in resolving the problems of ores associated with igneous rocks. Some of the problems associated with porphyry copper deposits have also been resolved by plate tectonics, although by no means all. Even other igneous-

**(a)**

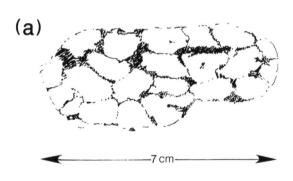

←———————7 cm———————→

**Figure 5.16**
(a) Tiny pull-apart fractures filled with serpentine in interstitial chromite between serpentinized olivine nodules.
(b) 'Frilled top' to a part of a small granular chromite band in dunite caused by segregation. Both specimens from Suleiman Range, Pakistan.

**(b)**

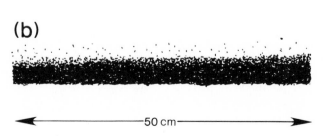

←———————50 cm———————→

associated ores have benefited from plate tectonic theory, but perhaps not always so completely. Perhaps what the idea of plate tectonics does illustrate, however, is that applied geology and academic geology both have their place in finding out how ores are formed and where to look for new ore fields.

It should be noted, however, that the largest (South Africa) and the fifth largest (Zimbabwe) producers of chromite, mine their ore from layered igneous complexes, namely the Bushveld Complex and the Great Dyke. These are not described here because they are adequately covered in textbooks concerned with the geology of igneous rock.

# CHAPTER 6

# Prospecting for ores

Although man has prospected ever since he needed stone for tools and pigments for decoration, most ancient discoveries were probably made by chance, just as many recent ones have been. The Romans had a reputation as prospectors, but the ores they mined had often been found long before they occupied the countries involved, Britain included. The law of *usufruct* effectively prevented them mining in their own homeland, so they exploited other people's finds elsewhere. Astonishingly, Agricola in his massive treatise on mining and metallurgy, *De Re Metallica* published in 1556, gave few guides to prospecting, despite the wide coverage allotted to other aspects of mining science. In truth, until the gold rush which followed the discovery of Californian gold at Sutter's Mill in 1849, most ore deposits were probably found more by luck than design.

California gold attracted optimistic immigrants from America, Europe, and even Asia, but few made fortunes from it. The others having learnt to prospect, went elsewhere. They found gold in Nevada, Colorado, and Utah in the USA; some went to Australia to find the Victoria goldfield, and later, the Golden Mile at Kalgoorlie-Coolgardie; by the end of the century, the Witwatersrand and Yukon goldfields had been discovered.

Californian gold established prospecting as a trade and developed a corps of professional prospectors. Most set their sights on gold, but they found other ores too by what is now called spin-off. These artisan prospectors continued well into the 20th century and were highly active during the Great Depression of the 1930s. But by then, companies were playing a larger role, using more refined methods based, at least to some extent, on geology. As companies have taken a larger and larger part in prospecting, so the numbers of independent prospectors have declined. Even so, many of the early uranium discoveries of 1945–1955 were made with cheap geiger counters wielded by amateur week-end prospectors, encouraged by generous government bonuses for the successful. Freelance prospectors still survive, especially in Canada, but they are a dying breed.

Prospecting today is a sophisticated pursuit. It incorporates a wide range of techniques. Teams of specialists work in the field, backed up by aircraft and helicopters. They are supported at base by workshops, laboratories and drawing offices, with accountants, lawyers, and economists available when needed. Such operations are beyond the resources of the old-fashioned prospector grub-staked by a small band of hopeful entrepreneurs. Prospecting is now Big Business.

## 6.1 Geological prospecting

Minerals are geological entities and every prospecting programme is, in effect, a specialized geological investigation. Geochemical, geobotanical, and geophysical methods may be used, but they support the geology, not replace it. The basis of all good prospecting is a geological map to guide every stage of the work. Map, map, map is the watchword, at ever increasing scales as a target is approached. But before anything can be done, the decision on what to look for, and where, must be made.

### 6.1.1 Choosing an area

Although it will not ignore anything else it may find, a company will usually start prospecting with specific metals in mind. Having decided what they want to look for, they must determine where it is most likely to be found. That is basically a geological question, and previous chapters have already shown that different metals occur in different geological environments. If we are to look for chromite, we look for ophiolites, if for copper, we have a wider choice, perhaps ophiolites again or, maybe, 50 km back from subduction zones where copper-bearing porphyries may occur. Small-scale geological maps may help us to decide where to go to discover brand new ore fields, but much prospecting is based on the prospector's dictum that 'If you want to shoot elephant, go to elephant country'. In other words, go where somebody else has already found what you are looking for. Such prospecting starts with a literature search, tracing reports of finds never followed up, of mining fields which have been abandoned, or even of fields still mining.

Some existing fields may show scope for new extensions outside the present working areas, possibly backed by new ideas of ore genesis. Old fields may have been abandoned because ore grades were too low; new methods of mining or treatment may make them productive again. Some were abandoned owing to a fall in metal price or political problems which no longer apply. In many cases, however, prospecting starts from scratch, or is based on reports of minerals found which have never been followed up. Kilembe Copper Mine in Uganda is an example. The first signs of copper were found in river gravels in the early 1920s, and noted in the Annual Report of the Geological Survey. A company read the report and prospected there in the 1930s but was not impressed. Another investigation was made in the early 1940s with similar results. More work was done in the late 1940s and early 1950s, but the mine did not come into production until 1954 when a railway reached the region and made mining worthwhile. Changing economic conditions and communications were the deciding factors.

### 6.1.2 Geological maps

A geological map is the basis of all good prospecting. National geological surveys produce maps, but their quality is variable; some are very good, some poor, some too small in scale to be useful. If maps are not adequate for prospecting, you must make your own.

Small-scale geological maps can be made from satellite images. Images can be obtained in a number of wavebands of which the near infrared is the most useful geologically. Alternatively, and better, are the computer-compatible tapes of the area, for then images can be instrumentally enhanced and presented on a VDU screen to bring out features which cannot be seen on the original images as received. The latest Landsat satellite (No. 5), the thematic mapper, has additional wavebands which show up those areas of clay alteration which surround epigenetic mineralization, and also distinguish gossans. Satellite imagery, however, can only give small-scale representation of the geology, picking out major rock formations and structures. Even so, small-scale maps are the first stage in selection and may indicate which parts of an area are worth closer investigation. Larger scale maps are needed to follow up; photogeology is often the answer.

Photogeology is a technique by which geology is interpreted from aerial photographs, using a stereoscope to give three-dimensional images. It can rapidly produce a geological map of considerable reliability and, depending on the scale of the photographs, great detail. Interpretation is accompanied by ground checking to identify rock formations. Many countries have complete photo-coverage at small scales (approx. 1:40,000) but it may be necessary to have prospecting areas rephotographed at larger scales. Scales as large as 1:5000 are possible. An airborne (as opposed to satellite) thematic mapper is now available, recording on eleven wave bands; other airborne methods of investigation include radar and thermal infra-red scanning.

The geological map is first used to eliminate from further examination any areas unlikely to be productive, such as where rocks are too young, or lithologically improbable, to have been mineralized. The second stage is to decide which areas are most likely to be mineralized, to look for lithologies, structures and intrusive rocks which might be ore-bearing. This is followed by ground investigation to search for any indications of ore, including gossans and rock alteration; but not all ore bodies crop out and sulphide ores are frequently leached close to the surface (section 2.2). Other methods may be needed.

## 6.2  Geochemical prospecting

In geochemical prospecting, trace amounts of metal are detected in stream sediments, soils or vegetation and used to guide the prospector to ore. Panning for gold, used for over 6000 years, is an ancient example (Fig. 6.1)

A single tiny 'colour' of gold, left after panning 10 kg of gravel represents less than 1 part per million (1 ppm) of the original sample but is detectable. Panning still survives, not only for gold, but for other heavy minerals, such as cassiterite, and even gem stones. Most geochemical prospecting, however, is now done by chemically analysing samples collected.

### 6.2.1  General principles

Geochemical prospecting is based on the principle that when a rock weathers to form soil, anything present in the rock will enter the soil. If the rock (and ore is

**Figure 6.1**
Panning a stream for heavy minerals. The gravel has been reduced to a small amount of concentrate which will now require careful panning to remove all but the heaviest minerals.

merely a rather rare rock) contains above normal amounts of metal, that will enter the soil too. Some metallic minerals oxidize to soluble products (section 2.3.1) and are spread in solution around their original source. They form an aureole of metal-enriched soil which is a larger target for a prospector to find than the original ore body. Vegetation also takes up some of the metal from the soil through its roots and enriches the humus when leaves are shed. Metals in solution will tend to move downhill in soil-water and eventually enter the drainage to form very low metal concentrations in streams. Some metallic minerals however, are insoluble and are spread into the soils around an ore body as particles which tend to move downhill with soil creep; they, too, eventually enter streams to be carried down-stream by water action. Metals in solution will tend to precipitate on the surface of minute iron and manganese oxide particles in the stream sediment, or by ion-exchange on clay minerals.

Thus metals are spread into soils, enriching them close to ore, are taken up by vegetation in the region of the ore, and migrate downhill and downstream of the ore.

### 6.2.2 Stream sediment sampling

Streams effectively sample the soils of the drainage basin, and so the first obvious choice of prospecting is to sample them. Fifty grams of active fine sediment are taken every 1 km or so along the streams and analysed for traces of metal. The results are plotted as symbols on a map of the drainage system (Fig. 6.2). Areas for further investigation soon becomes apparent.

In addition to fine sediment, coarser material may be panned and the heavy mineral concentrate analysed too. Although water can also be collected for

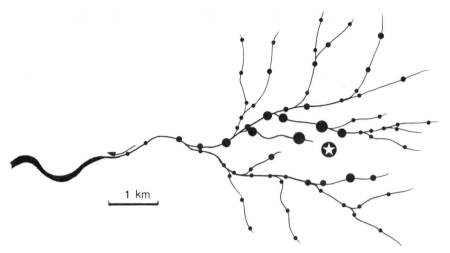

**Figure 6.2** Stream sediment sampling in a river system. The size of the black circles indicates the amount of metal found at each sample point, and suggests that ore occurs in the region shown by the white star.

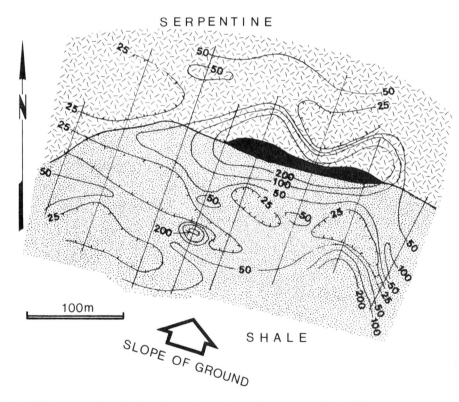

**Figure 6.3** A geochemical orientation survey in western Asia. The contours show the amount of cold-extractable copper in soils surrounding a small gossan. Analysis was done in camp up to a maximum of 200 ppm copper. Samples were taken every 10 m along the NNE-trending traverse lines shown.

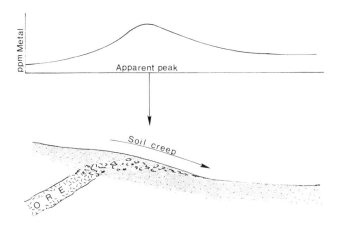

**Figure 6.4**
Geochemical anomalies may be displaced owing to downhill migration. The ore sub-outcrop is uphill of the anomaly.

analysis, there are problems. Metal content in streams may depend upon where rain is falling in the basin, and results can be difficult to interpret. Spring waters though, have been successfully sampled in some regions.

### 6.2.3 Soil sampling

Not all terrains are suitable for stream sediment sampling. African savannah, for instance, has poorly distributed and intermittent streams, and drainage is sometimes by wide, almost stagnant, papyrus swamps. For primary prospecting, soils can be sampled at 30–50 m intervals along traverse lines 300–500 m apart. Fifty gram samples of soil are again usually enough, collected at a predetermined depth. Soil may also be sampled at much closer intervals to follow up the results of other types of survey, geochemical, geological or geophysical. However, a geochemical anomaly does not mean that ore lies directly below it. There were many disappointments in the early days of geochemical prospecting because prospectors did not appreciate that anomalies are usually displaced by soil creep and by the movement of soil-water downhill (Fig. 6.4).

### 6.2.4 Soil gas

Oxidizing sulphides consume oxygen, so air contained in the soils above them is depleted in that element. Sulphuric acid is also generated during oxidation and will react with any carbonate in the soil to produce carbon dioxide. Air sucked from soils above sulphide ores should therefore be low in $O_2$ and high in $CO_2$. Air can be sucked out of the soils from about a metre depth using a probe and analysed on the spot with back-pack equipment. Not all climates are suitable; dryish climates provide better soil conditions than humid.

### 6.2.5 Geobotanic methods

Plants take up metals from soils. Some suffer damage and are stressed and stunted, with discoloured leaves; others will not grow at all. This is not a new discovery for Agricola noted that trees 'have a leaden look' near ore in *De Re Metallica* in 1556. On the other hand, some species of plants thrive on metal-rich soils. The copper flower, *Becium homblei*, grows on copper-rich soils in Zambia; California poppy likes similar soils in China. In northern Sweden, near the great iron mine at Kiruna, the Viscaria Copper Mine was discovered partly through recognition of the copper-loving alpine campion, *Viscaria alpinus*. Brooks (1983) lists 44 copper-loving plants, but other metals have their indicators too. Of particular note is the loco weed of cowboy literature, a poison vetch associated with 80 per cent of all Colorado plateau uranium deposits, its toxic properties due to its ability to extract selenium contained in the uranium ore minerals.

Plant material can also be ashed and analysed, but there are problems; for compatibility the same species must always be sampled at the same stage of growth — which is not always easy to recognize — and the plant may not be evenly distributed over the area of interest. Geobotany is a specialized subject and has yet to be fully developed.

### 6.2.6 Pathfinders

Pathfinders are elements which occur with an ore but are easier to detect than the ore mineral itself. For instance, arsenic occurs with many gold ores but, because it is more abundant than the gold, it is easier to find. Again, trace amounts of mercury occur with many sulphide ores. Mercury is very easy to detect in trace amounts and, because of its very high vapour pressure, its vapour will penetrate tens of metres of overburden, including boulder clay.

Comparatively simple instruments can be used in camp to determine parts per billion (ppb) quantities of mercury in soils. In one instrument, the sample is heated to emit mercury vapour which is passed over a thin film of gold. The mercury amalgamates with the gold and changes its electrical resistance, a tiny change which can be measured. The instrument is electronically controlled and analysis is largely a matter of button-pushing (Fig. 6.5). Alternatively a probe sucks soil gas out of an auger hole made in the soil and analyses it on the spot by a simple back-pack atomic absorption spectrometer. There are many pathfinders; one, radon gas, is described below (section 6.2.8).

### 6.2.7 Prospecting dogs

Dogs can be trained to sniff out iron and sulphide ores, and there has been at least one notable success in Finland. This form of prospecting works best in glaciated regions where ore at surface tends to be less altered. Russia and Canada also use trained dogs.

### 6.2.8 Radiometry

Radiometry, that is the measurement of radioactivity, is more conveniently considered here than under geophysics, to which it is equally related. Geiger-Muller counters were the first radiation detectors used and were carried by many successful week-end prospectors in the 1940s and 1950s. Scintillation counters are

**Figure 6.5**
A thin gold film mercury detector in use in camp. The instrument, made by Jerome Instrument Corporation, Arizona, USA, will detect parts per billion of mercury in soils.

now more usual; they are more sensitive, less affected by background 'noise' from cosmic radiation, and the better instruments discriminate between radiation from uranium, thorium, and potassium-40 ($^{40}K$). Portable models can be carried by a prospector on foot, or recording instruments can be mounted in a motor car, on a trawler's masthead, or used in an aeroplane.

Uranium is easy to detect at surface, but less so when under even a thin soil cover. This can be overcome by using radon as a pathfinder. Radon gas is a daughter element from the radioactive decay of uranium ($^{238}U \rightarrow {}^{226}Ra \rightarrow {}^{222}Rn$) and will rise through rocks and soils to the surface, even though the source may lie beneath the watertable. Radon has a half-life of 3.8 days and emits $\alpha$-particles as it decays. Particles can be counted by Trak-Etch.

In Trak-Etch, cheap plastic cups are place upside down in holes 60 cm deep spread over the area to be sampled and left in the ground for about three weeks, a period which allows fluctuations, caused by variations in barometric pressure and groundwater levels, to equalize. Each cup has a small piece of coated film (developed by the American Terradex Corporation) on its bottom which records tracks from $\alpha$-particles emitted by radon trapped in the cup (Fig. 6.6). The number of tracks on each sample film is a measure of the radioactivity. Trak-Etch has located ores situated over 150 m below surface. More sophisticated, but more expensive, $\alpha$-cups have now been developed using selenium detectors.

### 6.2.9 Rock geochemistry

Rock geochemistry is a relatively new approach to prospecting. It is based on determining the primary dispersion of metal in rock around ore, that is, traces of metal directly related to deposition of the ore, rather than its secondary dispersion in soils caused by weathering. It is more of a follow-up method than a primary prospecting tool, and relies heavily on pathfinders. Al Atia, for instance (Al Atia

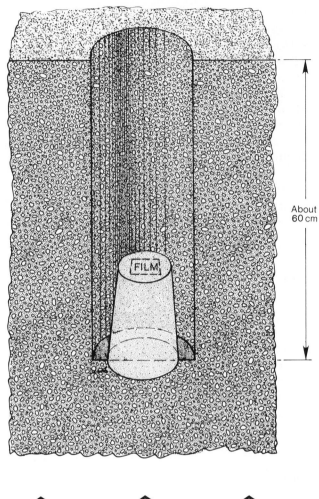

About
60 cm

**Figure 6.6**
A Trak-Etch cup placed in a
hole in the ground traps rising
radon gas. Radon releases
alpha-particles which leave
their track on film taped to the
inside of the cup.

RISING RADON GAS

and Barnes 1974), showed that the ratio of rubidium to potassium in rock in Wales
tended to increase as gold and gold-copper mineralization was approached.
Similar increases have been noted by Armbrust *et al.* (1977) in Chile, and by
others elsewhere.

### 6.2.10 Black boxes

There have been many attempts to design instruments which will analyse soils in
place. Most successful perhaps, is the berylometer, designed during the beryl-rush
of the early 1950s. This cumbersome instrument measured the beryllium content
of soil down to a depth of about 20 cm using the property that beryllium

emits neutrons when bombarded by gamma radiation. The gamma source was the isotope [124]Sb. In the 1960s the US government produced a jeep-mounted neutron activation spectrometer to detect gold and silver in soils in place, using [252]Cf as the neutron source to irradiate the soils. It does not appear to have been very successful in primary prospecting.

The PIF (Portable Isotope X-ray Fluorescence) analyser is a compact instrument which will measure the quantity of a number of metals in place, including in ores. Unfortunately sensitivity is, at best, in the range of hundredths of a per cent, which is insufficient for geochemical prospecting, although adequate for many other purposes, including borehole sampling. Other research developments include the field analysis of airborne dusts just above the surface in deserts, the analysis of mercury vapour above ground by aircraft, and the use of airborne lasers to excite fluorescent minerals, and detect them in daylight. The future holds promise for increased direct instrumentation in the field.

### 6.2.11 Chemical analysis

Trace amounts of metals in soils and other geochemical materials are nowadays analysed by three main methods; atomic absorption spectrometry (AA), emission spectrometry, and X-ray flourescence spectrometry (XRF). Smaller laboratories use AA as it is flexible and can be used for other analytical purposes too. Inductively coupled plasma mass spectrography (ICPMS), with its far better detection limits, now appears to have great potential in analysis, especially in regional geochemistry (Plant and Slater 1986). Laboratories devoted wholly to analysing geochemical samples tend to use very large emission spectrographs, which automatically record and print the results for perhaps 30 elements at a time. Even so, some organizations prefer to use field laboratories equipped with rather smaller spectrographs installed in trailer caravans. For rock geochemistry, XRF is especially suitable as samples require less preparation than do most other methods of rock analysis. For determining minute quantities of gold in rock, neutron activation analysis (NA) is best, but it is expensive and the laboratory must be within reach of an atomic pile where specimens can be irradiated.

Despite such sophisticated methods, useful results can be obtained by simple colorimetric analysis done in camp. The ability to analyse samples himself is an asset to a geologist should he need an immediate answer to a problem when hundreds of miles from a laboratory.

### 6.2.12 Assessing results

Geochemical prospecting can tell a geologist that anomalous amounts of metal occur in an area, and what those metals are. It cannot tell him the shape of the ore body or its size and grade. It merely tells him that certain metals occur within a defined area. Because of the spread of metals in the soils, and the displacement of anomalies on hillslopes, geochemical prospecting cannot always even give the geologist a target to drill. He must either dig trenches, or use geophysics. It is the task of the supervising geologist to decide which is the most economical method to locate a target, and a well-trained prospecting geologist will use any method available to him which will produce results.

In these days of computers, multi-element geochemical results can be programmed for a wide range of statistical methods. Even the contours of geochemical maps can be drawn by the computer to show the amounts of metals in soils or other materials. Geochemical prospecting is, however, only one tool in the geological armoury of prospecting techniques and must not be used to the exclusion of other methods.

## 6.3  Geophysical prospecting

Unlike geochemical prospecting, geophysical methods cannot tell you what metals occur in the ground, but they do tell you where a body is and its general shape and size. As in geochemical prospecting, the approach may be indirect, tracing not the ore minerals you are looking for, but minerals associated with them which are responsive to the methods in use.

Geophysics measures physical properties which are, as far as metallic ores are concerned, mostly confined to magnetism or electrical conductivity. There are other techniques; for instance, gravity surveying was used to delimit massive copper ore at Kalengwa in Zambia, and even seismic methods can be used to determine structure, but methods based on magnetism and electrical conductivity are the most important.

### 6.3.1 Magnetometry

Magnetite is the main magnetic mineral and magnetic methods have been used in prospecting since at least the development of magnetic iron ores in Swedish Lapland in the last century. Magnetometry has the advantage of being simple to apply and simple to interpret qualitatively. Basically, a magnetometer is used to measure the earth's magnetic field, and magnetic prospecting depends upon finding distortions to that field caused by strongly magnetic bodies.

Magnetic iron ores formed from magnetite are the most obvious targets, but magnetite is a minor constituent of other ores too, such as those of igneous metamorphic deposits. Disseminated magnetite in country rocks may reflect likely ore-bearing structures, or indicate intrusive rocks with which mineralization may be associated. Magnetometry is not always directed at the ore itself.

Magnetite is the most, but not the only, magnetic mineral. Pyrrhotite ($Fe_{1-n}S$) is almost as magnetic. As it often occurs with sulphide ores it can be used as a pathfinder to some types of copper, nickel, and gold bodies.

Unlike geochemical anomalies, magnetic anomalies are not displaced by soil creep. Magnetometry can therefore sometimes be used to follow up the investigation of a geochemical anomaly to find the true position of the possible ore and its attitude, so that holes can be drilled to confirm and sample it.

A wide range of magnetometers are on the market, from small hand-held instruments of low sensitivity (10 gamma), to proton-precession instruments which are far more precise (1 gamma) and almost as portable (Fig. 6.7).

**Figure 6.7**
A proton-precession magnetometer in use.

### 6.3.2 Electrical methods

There are a great many electrical methods of geophysical investigation. Resistivity
and self potential (SP) are the simplest for they need a minimum of equipment.
Resistivity measurements are made by passing current into the ground through
two electrodes, spaced from metres to hundreds of metres apart, depending on the
type of investigation. The current is picked up again by two additional electrodes
moved between them. Self potential uses earth currents generated by the oxidizing
sulphide ore body being sought, and traces them by two linked electrodes moved
systematically across the ground surface.

### 6.3.3 Electromagnetic prospecting

Electromagnetic (EM) methods of surveying depend on emitting a primary
electromagnetic field to induce currents in buried conductors. These induced

currents produce a secondary electromagnetic field of their own around the conductor, and their differences in phase and amplitude are measured. Both transmitter and signal receiver are coils, but the size of the coils vary widely with different methods. In Turam, the primary field is generated by laying a single cable on the ground in a huge square about 1 km across; smaller search coils are carried around inside it. At the other end of the scale is the EM gun in which primary and secondary coils are slung around the necks of two operators.

Some methods, such as AFMAG, use natural electromagnetic fields generated in the audiofrequency range by (often distant) thunderstorms. AFMAG is easy to use and interpret, although the results are imprecise. Another system (VLF) borrows the world-wide spread of very low frequency radio waves governments use to communicate with their submarines. Like AFMAG, it is easy to use.

All electromagnetic methods are directed at conductive ore bodies, in other words, ores with a high proportion of sulphide, usually in the process of oxidation. Ore bodies which contain only disseminated sulphides, such as porphyry copper deposits, must be treated by other methods.

### 6.3.4 Induced polarization

Induced polarization (IP) methods came onto the scene in the later 1950s when they were found particularly useful in tracing the extent of disseminated sulphide ore bodies. The theory is complex, but in effect, each isolated sulphide grain acts as an electrical condenser which is charged each time a short-lived electrical current is passed into the ground. The decay rate as these condensers discharge is measured. Alternating or direct current can be used, each giving different forms of information.

### 6.3.5 Airborne geophysical surveys

Some types of geophysical equipment can be flown over the ground in aircraft, recording geophysical conditions beneath. This gives rapid coverage of area and is particularly useful in those parts of the world where field seasons are short, such as the arctic regions of Canada, or where terrain is difficult to traverse on the ground, as in tropical forest. The main instruments used are magnetometers, EM systems, and scintillation counters.

The aircraft flies traverse lines approximately 1 km apart, recording geophysical measurements for later interpretation. If only magnetic readings are needed, the plane may fly at several thousand metres, depending on the detail required. However, if EM and radiometric measurements are to be made, flying height must be reduced so that instruments are within 150 to 200 m of the ground. This ground contact has to be maintained by flying uphill and down dale, following the land contours with the aid of a radioaltimeter, leaving little glide path should engine failure occur; insurance rates tend to be high! The flight path and position of the aircraft is controlled by Doppler navigation. With such low flying, survey is restricted to flat or gentle rolling country for, although helicopters can fly mountainous regions, the cost is too high except for limited areas.

To obtain maximum separation of coils for airborne EM surveying,

(a)

Stinger                                    Stinger

(b)

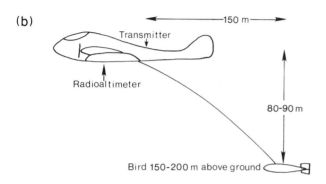

←————150 m————→

Transmitter

Radioaltimeter

80–90 m

Bird 150–200 m above ground

(c)

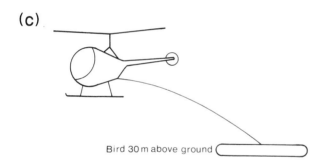

Bird 30 m above ground

**Figure 6.8**
Different airborne geophysical
systems showing methods of
separating coils or removing
instruments from influence of
the aircraft. Coils can also be
mounted on wing-tips of larger
aircraft.

transmitters and receivers are mounted either in opposite wing tips, or in stingers
in nose and tail (Fig. 6.8). Alternatively one instrument is trailed as a bird at the
end of a cable behind the plane to give even greater separation.

Airborne geophysical surveys produce a mass of magnetic, electromagnetic,
and radiometric information which, when interpreted, indicate a large number
of geophysically anomalous zones which must be investigated. Most anomalies
will eventually be found to have nothing to do with ore at all; some conductive
bodies may be merely basic dykes with water in their joints acidified by the
oxidation of pyrite, others may be graphite bands in schists. What airborne survey
does do is to quickly produce a number of prospecting targets to be investigated
further, thus concentrating work to limited areas.

Follow up investigation of anomalies can take a number of directions. Lower
level geophysical survey may be done using helicopter-borne instruments (Fig.
6.8) but, more usually, follow-up will consist of a mixture of ground geophysics,
detailed geochemical prospecting, and geology.

The next developments in airborne prospecting will almost certainly be in
multispectralscanning, flying at 2000–3000 m. *World Mining Equipment* (1986)

**Figure 6.9**
Drilling an inclined hole. Diamond drill rods 4 m long are stacked against the derrick ready for coupling to the drill string.

reports on recent successful trials in Australia of equipment recording 15 spectral bands, including short wave and thermal infra-red. The plane scans a flight path swathe 4 km wide, separately processing each 10 m$^2$ of ground beneath.

## 6.4  Detailed follow-up

Once anomalous results from the various methods of prospecting have shown the promise of ore, the task of finding out as much as possible about it follows. Only 2 per cent of all promising prospects ever become mines, and fewer than half of those actually make a profit. It is therefore essential to find out as much as possible as cheaply as possible. Geophysics may be able to outline a geometry so that boreholes can be positioned to the best advantage. Drilling may be by diamond drilling (Fig. 6.9) which can be done at any angle and can be recover cores of rock and ore from the hole for examination and assay (analysis), or it may be churn or percussion drilling, where only chips and ground-up rock flour are recovered from the always vertical holes. In many cases, the cheaper churn drilling is adequate.

The surface extent of the ore must also be investigated by trenching across it or by sinking deep pits. The sub-outcrop, however, may be deeply altered by oxidation and leaching, and shallow shafts may have to be sunk to fresher material from which exploratory workings can be driven to examine the ore (Fig. 6.10). Alternatively, an adit may be driven down-slope from the outcrop to intersect ore

**Figure 6.10** A gold-bismuth prospect shaft in East Africa. Waste is raised in a kibble (bucket) by hand-windlass.

at deeper levels (Fig. 6.11). Exploratory workings are sampled and geologically mapped at 1:500, or larger, to see what information they can provide (Fig. 6.12), and bulk samples of several tonnes may also be taken for milling tests, so that methods of beneficiation can be planned.

Further drilling is needed to confirm that sufficient ore occurs to warrant mining. Drilling also shows the shape and attitude of the ore body so that mining can be planned; this has to be done as carefully as for any other industrial enterprise. Surface plant, offices and housing need to be designed, and sources of power, fuel, and water investigated. As mines are often in remote areas, roads, railways, and landing fields may have to be constructed and schools, churches, mosques, shops, football fields, and other amenities provided for the people who are to work there. The geologist must find the materials to make them.

Geology is mapped in great detail at every stage of mine development. Cross-sections are compiled and three-dimensional models are constructed. The geologist must solve day-to-day problems, such as relocating faulted-off parts of the ore and tracing folded structures. He must also determine what structural and lithological features control ore deposition and see how they may affect ore grade and composition. Geological mapping does not cease when the mine goes into production. Always there is the need to look for more ore, either as extensions to the known ore body or as new bodies which, because they do not crop out, are inferred only on geological grounds. The composition of the ore must also be continually monitored. It may vary laterally or vertically; such changes are often geologically predictable and, if recognised well in advance, mining methods and milling plant can be modified to accommodate them.

**Figure 6.11**
An exploration adit in East Africa driven to intersect a sulphide vein beneath a gossan found on a ridge top.

**Figure 6.12**
Mapping underground geology. Most mapping is done with only miners' lamps for illumination. Further difficulty is caused by mine walls coated with fine wet dirt produced by drilling and blasting.

**Table 6.1** Sequence of stages in prospecting.

| Stage | Place | Operation |
|---|---|---|
| 1 | Office | Site selection: literature search; examination of satellite imagery. |
| 2 | Office/field | Prospecting: photogeology and ground checking; examining existing maps; planning fieldwork; eliminating and selecting areas from maps. |
| 3 | Field | Prospecting hopeful areas: geochemical, geophysical, and geobotanical surveys; geological mapping. Alternatively, airborne geophysical survey followed by ground geophysics and geochemistry; geological mapping. |
| 4a | Field | Follow-up: detailed geophysical and geochemical investigation of anomalies found, with geological mapping; possibly helicopter geophysics; trenching, pitting, and drilling of hopeful sites. |
| 4b | Field | Further follow-up: detailed mapping of confirmed mineralization; prospect shafts dug and adits driven and mapped; sampling done and possibly bulk samples taken for milling tests. |
| 5a | Field/office | Feasibility: further drilling; assessment of grade and tonnage; some underground development and more bulk sampling for mill testing. Decision to mine: search for sources of water, power, fuel, labour and for building materials; and limestone etc. for mill, possibly for smelting fluxes. |
| 5b | Office | Planning: mine and plant design, including mill (and smelter?); raising capital; legal/leasing arrangements. |
| 6 | Site | Development: mine development, building and equipping power plant, mill, workshops, offices, making roads, building houses, and amenities; possibly building smelter and dam for water storage and/or power. |
| 7 | Site | Mining. |

Many abandoned mines have not been geologically surveyed and the records of many have been lost, destroyed, are unavailable, or are held in the offices of competing companies whose base may even be in another country. Often, geologists have to map and sample abandoned mines for companies which hope to re-open them. Such expeditions can sometimes be adventurous, to say the least! Earlier, it was said that the dictum for successful prospecting is map, map, map. This cannot be repeated often enough; the more that is known of the geology, the less likely is money to be wasted on the search. A summary of the operations required for a prospecting programme is shown in Table 6.1.

# CHAPTER 7

# Fossil fuels and hot rocks

Peat, coal, oil and natural gas are called the fossil fuels because they are formed from what was once organic matter. They provide us with the major part of the energy we use today. Oil shales and tar sands are also fossil fuels; at present they supply only a tiny fraction of our energy needs but, with time, they will almost certainly become major contributors. Other energy sources include uranium and hydroelectric power, but as neither are fossil fuels, they are not considered here. We will, however, look at the energy available from thermal springs. Italy, Iceland and New Zealand have long tapped these geothermal sources and other countries are developing them, too. Experiments are now being conducted to tap the internal heat of the earth by pumping water down boreholes in areas of high geothermal gradient and retrieving it as steam. The need to provide energy for a rapidly increasing world population is a problem that future generations must face, and it is the geologist who will have to find sources for most of it.

## 7.1  Oil and gas

Oil and gas are related substances composed of the same two elements — carbon and hydrogen — merely arranged in different molecular structures resulting in different physical states. Tars, bitumens, waxes and asphalts fall into the same group, and oil shales and tar sands have a close affinity.

### 7.1.1  History of oil and gas

Oily substances have a long history. Bitumen was used as the mortar between the bricks in the walls of ancient Jericho 2700 years ago and ancient Egyptians used it to caulk their boats and to mummify their dead. The fire-worshipping Zoroastrian and Parsee religions originally developed around the eternal fires of Baku on the shores of the Caspian Sea, where gas seeps had been ignited by natural causes; fires of the oracles had a similar history, and a seep at Chimaera in Turkey has burnt continuously for 2500 years (Brinkman 1976). Not only gas, but oil seeps had their uses too; the Romans were probably not the first, and certainly were not the last, to use such oil in their lamps. To round off this ancient history, it was in 200 BC that the Chinese drilled the first oil well although, to be fair, they were drilling for brine!

The modern history of oil began in 1859 when 'Colonel' Drake struck oil in a well only 22 m deep at Oil Creek in Pennsylvania, USA. Drilling was sponsored by Professor Silliman (of sillimanite fame) and friends. The Drake Well marks the birthplace of the modern oil industry.

Within a few years of Drake's success, numerous wells had been sunk in Pennsylvania, in other parts of the USA, and in many other countries. Even so, by the start of World War II, some 80 years later, oil production was still largely confined to USA, Venezuela, the Carribean, Iran-Iraq, Romania, and the USSR. Since then, fields have been found all over the world, from the North Slope of Alaska to southeastern Australia (Fig. 7.1).

Gas has a slightly different modern history. As long ago as 1821 parts of New York were lit by gas from a well 9 m deep! The problem with developing the natural gas industry was distribution. Most oil wells produced gas as a by-product but, as it could only be distributed locally, most of it had to be flared (burnt) off to get rid of it. The break-through came in the 1930s when cheap seamless steel pipe came onto the market to make distribution easier. Now gas is piped hundreds of kilometres over land and under sea in welded pipes over a metre in diameter; or it is liquified under pressure and shipped by sea as LPG and LNG (liquid petroleum and liquid natural gas). Distribution is no longer a problem.

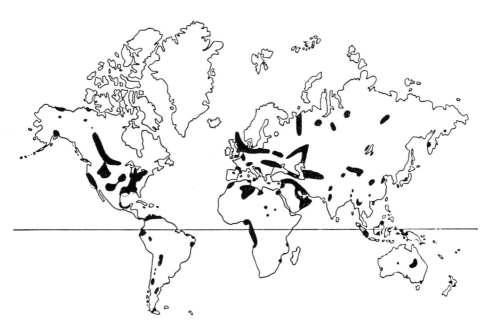

**Figure 7.1**  The main known oil- and gas-bearing areas of the world.

### 7.1.2 The 'mineralogy' of oil

Crude oil emerging from a well is a hot, yellow, brown or green liquid with an unpleasant smell. When cool, it may be free flowing or as viscous as syrup; some is almost solid. Crude oil is a mixture of hydrocarbons consisting of about 80 per cent alkanes and cycloalkanes; and the rest aromatics and impurities. Impurities include ash, helium, hydrogen, nitrogen, carbon dioxide, and hydrogen sulphide or sour gas. Helium is a valuable commodity, and the hydrogen sulphide provides by-product sulphur. Not all oils contain sour gas, only those from carbonate (limestone and dolomite) reservoirs. Those free of it are termed sweet.

Alkanes, cycloalkanes and aromatics are hydrocarbon groups, each formed of a large number of closely related compounds composed only of hydrogen and carbon atoms in different types of molecular structure. Each quadrivalent carbon atom can bond with four monovalent hydrogen atoms or link with two other carbon atoms. The greater the number of carbon atoms in a compound, the higher the boiling and freezing points and the heavier the compound.

(a) *Alkanes.*    Alkanes are formed from chains of carbon atoms, each carbon atom with attached hydrogen atoms. The simplest is methane, which has only one carbon and four hydrogen atoms. As additional carbon atoms are added to a chain, so the compound changes. Each carbon atom in a chain also holds two hydrogen atoms except for those at the ends of the chain which link to three (Fig. 7.2a). Short chains with four carbon atoms or less are gases; chains of up to 14 carbon atoms are liquids; the remainder, with up to 60 carbon atoms, are waxy solids and bitumens (i.e. asphalts, pitches and tars).

Alkanes have the general chemical formula of $C_nH_{2n+2}$. Methane gas, $CH_4$, is the lightest member of the series, ethane, propane and butane have lengthening chains and are therefore heavier. Butane is only just gas at normal temperatures and pressures. It can be easily liquified by a slight increase in pressure and bottled; hence its popularity as camping gas.

The chains of some alkanes branch to form isomers, that is compounds with the same chemical composition but with slight differences in structure and therefore slightly different chemical and physical properties (Fig. 7.2b). Older texts refer to the alkanes as the paraffin series, a term still used by many.

(b) *Cycloalkanes.*    Sometimes called napthenes or cyclo-paraffins, the cycloalkanes are formed of rings of three, four, five or more carbon atoms, each carbon having two attached hydrogen atoms to give the general formula $C_nH_{2n}$ (Fig. 7.2c). Side chains can replace the hydrogen atoms as with the aromatics described below. Cycloalkanes are liquid at normal temperatures and pressures and make up about 40 per cent of crude oil.

(c) *Aromatics.*    Aromatics have the general formula $C_nH_{2n-6}$, but only those compounds based on the benzene ring of six carbon atoms are important here (Fig. 7.2d). Benzene rings average 1 ½ bonds between the carbon atoms, leaving only six bonds to attach to hydrogen atoms to give the formula $C_6H_6$. The hydrogen atoms, however, can be replaced by side chains to form new compounds (Fig.

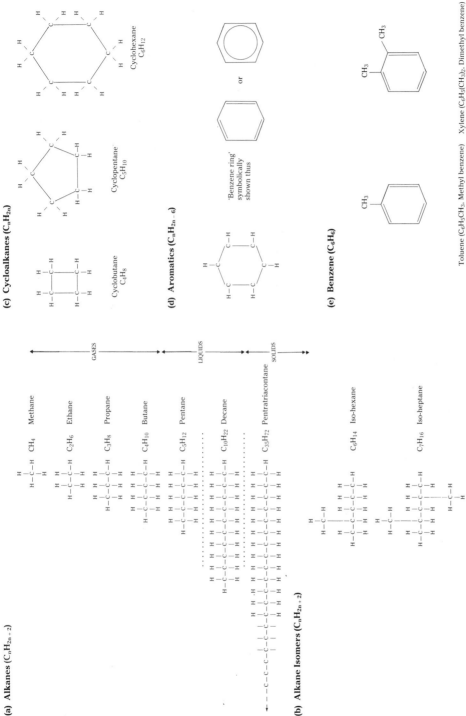

**Figure 7.2** The chemistry of petroleum. (a) How the alkanes form ever-lengthening chains. (b) Examples of alkane isomers formed by the replacement of hydrogen atoms by side chains; the new compounds have the same chemical composition but different properties. (c) The three main cycloalkanes. (d and e) The benzene compounds most commonly found in petroleum.

7.2e), the commonest being methyl benezene (toluene) by the attachment of one methyl group ($CH_3$, i.e. methane $CH_4$ minus one hydrogen atom), and dimethyl benezene, or xylene, by the attachment of two methyl groups. In xylene, the methyl radicals can be attached to adjacent or non-adjacent corners of the ring, giving three isomers. Benzene, toluene, and xylene are the commonest aromatics found in petroleum, increasing from minor amounts in light oils to over 25 per cent in heavier crudes.

Crude oils are formed of various mixtures of these compounds, with the gasses and solids dissolved in the liquids. Some fields produce only dry gas, that is methane alone; a few yield condensate, a gas which sheds oil as temperatures and pressures drop on reaching the surface. Most fields, however, give liquid petroleum (gasoline) oils containing some dissolved gas and solids. Some oils occur saturated with gas and are found associated with free petroleum gas (methane to butane). As a general rule, old oils are light oils, young ones are heavy.

### 7.1.3 The oil industry

In the early years of the petroleum industry crude oils recovered from wells were fractionally distilled and the condensates gave products of different volatilities. Petroleums, paraffins (kerosenes), diesel oils, engine oils, lubricants, and fuel oils were produced, leaving a residue of waxes and bitumens. Not all these products were equally saleable in the quantities produced. Thermal cracking to break long chains down to lighter, shorter chain compounds, was the next advance, giving more marketable yields from heavier oils. Later still, oils were chemically reformed to yield isomers; alkanes were converted to cycloalkanes; cycloalkanes to aromatics. Processing now produces not only petroleum fuels and oils in numerous different grades, but also feedstock for the huge petrochemical industry which supplies us with plastics, synthetic rubbers, resins, solvents, man-made fibres, detergents, fungicides, paints, and many other materials in daily use. Petroleum is not merely a fuel, it is part of the chemical industry.

### 7.1.4 Formation of petroleum

Several origins have been attributed to petroleum, including its formation from carbon and hydrogen from the mantle. Small amounts may have been formed that way but the bulk of all oil now used was generated from organic matter at temperatures of less than 200°C. This is demonstrated by the presence of chlorophyll-like vegetable porphyrins which break down at 200°C. It is now generally accepted that petroleum is derived largely from the free-floating (vegetable) phytoplankton which thrives in the seas to a depth of about 120 m from the surface. The sequence of events which leads to oil formation is as follows.

1 Phytoplankton die; normally their remains sink to lower levels where they oxidize and the products disperse. In limited conditions, the water is stratified, with stagnant anoxic water lying below the oxygenated upper levels. Plankton-remains which sink to these lower anoxic levels do not oxidize but are preserved to form organic-rich bottom muds. The Black Sea, whose muds consist of 30 per cent organic matter, are a present-day example of an oil-forming environment.

2 The organic material in the muds suffers bacterial breakdown during diagenesis as the muds become buried by later deposits. Protein, etc., is degraded to form kerogen. Kerogen includes a range of complex hydrocarbon substances which also contain oxygen, nitrogen and sulphur, and is found in many sedimentary rocks, such as bituminous limestones, oil shales and tar sands. Kerogens formed from plankton differ from those derived from algae or land plants: consequently, the difference in sources material affects any petroleum products formed from them.

3 As sediments become more deeply buried and temperature and pressure increase, oxygen, nitrogen and sulphur are lost. Kerogens break down to more oily substances. When burial has reached 1 km, temperature has risen to about 65°C and katagenesis occurs with the formation of long-chain hydrocarbons; as temperatures increase further, these hydrocarbons are thermally cracked to shorter chains, with bentonitic clays acting as catalysts (bentonite is also the catalyst used in oil refineries). The early-formed oils are heavy oils, the later ones lighter. The maximum release of oil is when burial reaches the oil window between 1 km and 3 km, with temperature of about 175° (Fig. 7.3). During this time, gas has also been forming and, as depth increases below 3 km, more and

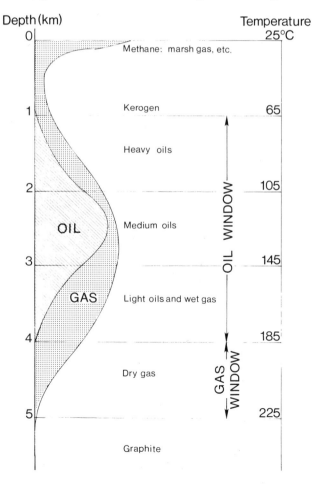

**Figure 7.3**
The relationship between depth of burial, temperature, and the petroleum products formed (adapted from several sources).

more gas forms and less and less liquid oil. At about 4 km deep, dry gas forms (the gas window), but most dry gas originates from more woody material than that which forms the usual petroleum gases; exploitable dry gas fields, such as those in the North Sea, are mainly derived from deeply buried coal.

4 Metagenesis is the final stage. At about 5 km all hydrogen is lost and only carbon, in the form of graphite, is left.

### 7.1.5 Primary migration

To form an oilfield, oil must first be expelled from its impermeable mudstone source rocks and then migrate via more permeable rocks to accumulate in reservoirs in recoverable amounts. At what stage this happens is, in the words of Selley '. . . still not clear . . .' (1985, p. 204). It is all too easy to assume that oil leaves its source rocks as the waters of compaction are squeezed out of them during diagenesis and lithification. Yet oil is only formed after most of the pore water has already been lost. More likely, the oil is expelled with water released by the change of clay minerals from montmorillionite to illite which occurs at about 110°C, right in the middle of the oil window (op. cit. p. 200).

The manner in which oil (or gas) is carried out of its source rocks is equally obscure. Some suggest it migrates as a protopetroleum of partially-formed oils still soluble in brine. Fully-formed petroleum compounds are not generally water soluble, but solubility does increase with rise in temperature, most markedly with hydrocarbons having a carbon number of 10 (such as decane, $C_{10}H_{22}$), or less. With source rock temperatures in the region of 100°C this might account for light hydrocarbons being taken into solution, but not for heavier ones. A third suggestion is that natural detergent-like organic compounds called micelles might carry oil out in colloidal solution. However, micelles are not abundant, and they are molecularly larger than the pore size of most source rocks. As Selley says, 'The exact process of primary migration . . . is obscure'. (op. cit. p. 211).

### 7.1.6 Secondary migration

Once oil has been expelled from its source rocks, it migrates through sandstone or carbonate aquifers by the movement of formation water brines until it reaches a geological structure — a trap — from which it can move no further. During migration oil, if in collodial or micellar solution, is shed into the brine as tiny droplets. Droplets contact other droplets in the brine-filled rocks to form larger droplets. Oil is lighter than the brine and the droplets rise through it wherever they have opportunity to do so within the porous medium they are passing through. In granular rocks, droplets may eventually coalesce until they are locked into the rock because they have become larger than the throats between the grain pores; they can then move no further. A fall in pressure due to any one of a number of geological reasons may cause the drops to expand within their pores owing to the gas dissolved within them, and so they may contact adjacent drops in adjacent pores. By coalescence, a continuous stringer of oil may form in the rock and, if it reaches a specific 'critical height', the stringer will rise owing to its buoyancy within the surrounding brine, collecting more and more droplets on its journey, so rising faster and faster as it grows in height (Fig. 7.4). Critical height depends

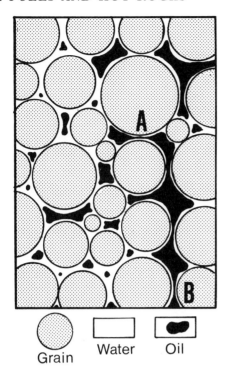

**Figure 7.4**
Oil in a water-wet sandstone. Droplets in pores between A and B have coalesced to form a stringer. When a stringer reaches the critical height it will rise, gathering velocity as it collects more droplets and increases its height.

Grain     Water     Oil

on throat size, viscosity of the oil, and density of both oil and brine. The finer the porous medium, the greater the critical height, sometimes several metres. The medium must be water(brine)-wet; and stringers may still be influenced by lateral currents in the brine so that the stringer does not rise vertically but as a vector of current and buoyancy. Oil accumulates when the stringer can move no further.

Porosity is theoretically a maximum of 48 per cent in uncemented sand composed of perfectly sorted spherical grains loosely packed. This is, of course, never attained. Grain size does not affect porosity but it does influence throat size and, therefore, critical height. Packing, degree of sorting, grain shape, and cement all affect porosity in granular rocks. Permeability and porosity in carbonate rocks is generally less restricted; it depends on solution-enlarged pathways along bedding and joints, fossil casts, stylolites, and porous reef materials. Shrinkage caused by dolomitization also helps. Oolitic limestone, with an intergranular porosity, has the best of both worlds.

### 7.1.7 Reservoirs

Reservoirs are structural traps which prevent oil migrating further and allow it to accumulate. They consist of a brine-saturated permeable formation overlain by an impermeable unit which seals the oil in place. About 60 per cent of all reservoir rocks are sandstones, the remainder limestones and dolomites, with a tiny proportion of other permeable rocks and, in at least one instance, jointed granite. Sealants include shales and mudstones and, especially in the Middle East, gypsum and salt-bearing marl formations. Salt also seals (some) oil pools associated with salt domes.

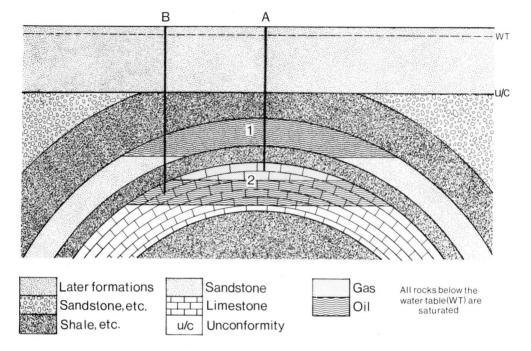

| | Later formations | | Sandstone | | Gas | All rocks below the |
| :-- | :-- | :-- | :-- | :-- | :-- | :-- |
| | Sandstone, etc. | | Limestone | | Oil | water table(WT) are saturated |
| | Shale, etc. | u/c | Unconformity | | | |

**Figure 7.5**   A bald-headed anticline. Later formations above an unconformity conceal the structure. Note that reservoir 1 has oil but no free gas. Reservoir 2 has free gas above a gas-saturated oil. Well A would tap only gas in reservoir 2 until all gas was expended, but oil would be driven up well B by the pressure of gas above it.

Eighty per cent of reservoirs are anticlinal domes (periclines). They contain three fluid phases; gas at the top, brine at the bottom, and oil between them. However, the phase boundaries are not distinct, and some brine is present throughout the whole reservoir. If the migration path and reservoir rocks were not water(brine)-wet, the oil could not migrate nor accumulate in them. A typical oil structure is shown in Figure 7.5.

An oil pool, that is, an individual accumulation of oil in an oilfield, can be of oil with some gas dissolved in it, oil saturated with gas and accompanied by free gas, or condensate gas from which oil will condense when temperatures and pressures change (i.e., on reaching the surface). There are also pools of dry gas. Oils in carbonate reservoirs are contaminated with sour gas (hydrogen sulphide) formed by the biogenic breakdown of anhydrite and gypsum in the presence of methane, reactions we have met before:

$$CH_4 + CaSO_4.2H_2O \longrightarrow CaCO_3 + H_2S + 3H_2O \text{ (for gypsum)}$$
$$CH_4 + CaSO_4 \longrightarrow CaCO_3 + H_2S + H_2O \text{ (for anhydrite)}$$

Although most oil occurs in anticlines, there are other types of trap and a selection is shown in Figure 7.6. Reefs are perhaps the most important of these, either as the roughly circular, but often very tall, bioherms, or as longitudinal barrier reef-like bisotromes such as the Guadalupe-Capitan reef in New Mexico

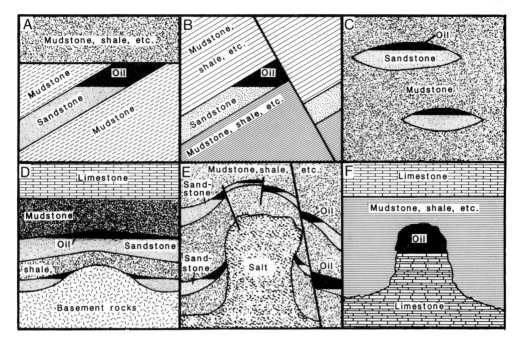

**Figure 7.6** Typical oil structures. A an unconformity trap; B a fault trap; C string sands formed in a muddy estuary; D a compactional anticline above a hill in the basement topography; E a variety of traps associated with a salt dome; F a biohermal reef.

which is hundreds of kilometres long. Salt domes are important reservoir formers in some parts of the world and there are numerous varieties of fault and sedimentary traps. Many fields consist of a combination of traps.

### 7.1.8 Recovery of oil

Oil is recovered by drilling. Modern oilfields are not, however, the forests of abandoned wooden derricks so frequently shown in films of the early days of oil exploitation in Texas, although many of the public still seem to think this is so whenever onshore drilling is suggested in Britain. Derricks are now made of steel, and are expensive; they are dismantled and moved when their job is done. Nor are leases let out to hosts of entrepreneurs any more. Figure 7.7 shows a modern onshore oil rig, much larger than the ore exploration drill shown in Figure 6.9. Figure 7.8 shows derricks in California disguised as buildings to reduce the environmental impact. Successful holes, once drilled, are often marked only by a nodding donkey pump (Fig. 7.9). Offshore drilling is more difficult and much more expensive than onshore. To save costs, 20 holes may be sunk from a single platform position by deflecting the holes from the vertical to radiate outwards from the sea floor.

When a drill penetrates a reservoir in the oil column beneath the gas cap, oil is driven up the well-hole by the pressure of gas above it (gas drive) and by the pressure of water below it (water drive see Fig. 7.5). Not all wells have sufficient

**Figure 7.7**
An onshore oil rig. Drill pipe is stacked in the derrick; the higher the derrick, the longer their length and the quicker they can be taken out of the well and returned to it when changing bits or collecting core. The rig is easily dismantled, moved and reassembled at a new site. Derricks are not left on site as wooden ones were in the past.
(Photo by D.J. Barnes)

pressure to drive oil to the surface and all eventually have to be pumped. Gas separated from oil at the surface is sometimes pumped back into the ground to help to drive more oil up, or water may be injected beneath to improve water drive. Even so, only 20–40 percent of oil can normally be recovered from a reservoir, although secondary recovery methods may increase this a little; a great deal of research is in progress to improve recoveries. Gas flows much more easily and up to 90 per cent can be covered.

### 7.1.9 Oil exploration

There is a fundamental difference between looking for oil and prospecting for coal or metals; oil seldom crops out. Only a few oil fields (Baku with its eternal fires is one of them) are marked by oil or gas seeps. Most reservoirs lie deep, without surface indications. Half of all oil recovered is from depths of 1–2.5 km, some from

**Figure 7.8** Drill rigs camouflaged as apartment blocks at Long Beach, California, USA.

**Figure 7.9** A nodding donkey pumping oil from a well to adjacent storage tanks at Signal Hill, Long Beach, California, USA.

as much as 3.5 km down. However, the search for oil does not have advantages over prospecting for ores. Oil fields are confined to sedimentary basins, and 85 per cent of all oil is in Mesozoic or younger rocks, that is in formations less than 230 Ma old; 60 per cent of it is in rocks less than 50 Ma old.

Satellite imagery and photogeology can help to identify and map these sedimentary basins. Geological fieldwork, however, is less intensive and on a broader scale than in the search for ores, for the target is deeply buried. The first approach is to decide whether a basin is ever likely to have had a sedimentary environment favourable to oil formation and, if so, to locate source rocks which have matured and been buried and heated sufficiently to have generated oil. From rock samples it is now possible to estimate the type and quantity of hydrocarbon generated in them, and when it was expelled. The next task is to locate favourable traps. Drilling is an essential part of oil prospecting but it is expensive and, wherever possible, geophysical methods are used to map the subsurface, be it under land or sea. Gravity and magnetic surveys play their part but seismic methods are the mainstay of oil prospecting. Geophysics does not, of course, locate oil, it merely locates favourable structures which might contain it.

To prove oil, wells must be sunk, sometimes as much as 3 km, deep, a few even deeper. Very deep holes may start with a diameter of nearly a metre, reducing in stages to about 18 cm towards the bottom. As the well is drilled, cores or chippings of rock penetrated are examined to identify formations and date them from their fossils, particularly the microfossils. Specially trained geologists called mudloggers monitor the progress of the well with a complex of computerized instruments. They measure drilling rates and pressures, and a gas chromatograph continuously records the level of hydrocarbons present in the formations penetrated. An important aspect of mudlogging (from which it gets its name) is the monitoring of the amount and consistency of the heavy drilling mud used to lubricate the drill and to contain the gas pressures which might cause blow-outs. Beckmann (1976) gives an excellent account of what mudloggers and geologists do on drilling rigs and the instruments they use.

Much geological logging of wells is adapted from geophysical techniques used on the surface. Self potential and resistivity methods, differential gamma-ray logging, and neutron activation with isotope neutron sources, are all used in wells to correlate formations; even porosites of formations penetrated can be measured in the hole.

Petroleum exploration is expensive and, like the lone gold prospector of old, the entrepreneurial wild catter who drilled on hunches and hope, has passed into history. Only large companies can now afford to prospect for oil. However, the traditional oil industry is meeting an increasing challenge from syncrude oil, that is oil obtained from processing tar sands, oil shales and coal. The cost of syncrudes was fast becoming competitive with Gulf crudes until the dramatic fall in oil prices in 1986.

## 7.2  Tar sands

Tar sands represent a huge potential source of energy, possibly as much as $2.5 \times 10^{22}$ joules, equivalent to the total remaining reserves of oil and gas (Skinner 1976). Tar sands are thus one of the alternative energy sources, capable of producing a syncrude oil from which all the usual oils and petrochemicals can be extracted. At present, only the Athabasca basin sands of Northeastern Alberta, Canada, are exploited, but they alone contribute 10 per cent of all oil consumed in Canada. The Athabasca reserves are huge, for the McMurray formation tar sands average over 40 m thick and cover 75,000 km². Other countries have tar sands too, including those at Olenik in USSR, the Orinoco in Venezuela, and Bemulanga in Malagasy, all similar in extent to the deposits in Canada.

### 7.2.1 Composition

The Athabasca sands are typical. They consist of deltaic quartz sands impregnated with about 11 per cent of a heavy viscous bitumen which contains about 60 per cent oil, 30 per cent resins, and a residue of asphaltenes.

### 7.2.2 Origin

The origin of tar sands is debatable. The most obvious theory suggests that erosion has unroofed reservoirs in an oilfield and that the escaping oil has been carried by rivers into a delta where it mixed with sands. Its lighter hydrocarbons were lost by evaporation before being buried by later deposits, leaving the heavy tarry residues. Oilfields do occur east of Athabasca, and other theories suggest seepage westwards through porous rocks into the deltaic sands. It has even been suggested that bitumens are immature oils which were never buried deep enough to complete their maturation; this is unlikely for the oil is too viscous to have moved into the sands by secondary migration. Another theory is that reservoirs beneath the sea floor leaked oil; the oil rose to the surface and was windblown into tidal lagoons to pollute the sands, just as British and other beaches have recently been contaminated by wrecked oil tankers. Smaller bitumen pools, such as those first exploited by 17th century buccaneers in Trinidad to caulk their ships, are more easily explained by seepage of oil from underlying near-surface oil pools. Evaporation of the lighter hydrocarbons has left only the tarry residues.

### 7.2.3 Production

The Athabasca tar sands are strip-mined at a rate of 6000 tonnes/hr by draglines and bucket-wheel excavators. The sands are stratified, with a few thin beds containing less than 6 per cent bitumen but the remaining 85 per cent of the sand is ore grade. The sand is processed at site to extract the syncrude, which is then piped 500 km to Edmonton for refining.

## 7.3  Oil shales

Oil shale is a fine-grained, hard (H = 5), dense, dark clay-rock or siltstone which contains better than 10 per cent kerogen. It may be any age from Palaeozoic upwards and occurs in many countries, many of them not otherwise oil-producers. Oil was extracted from shales in the Midland Valley of Scotland from 1850 to 1964 and in Alsace from as early as 1755. USSR and China are two current producers, while Estonia recovers 16 million tonnes of syncrude a year. Brazil is a recent comer to large-scale oil shale mining and has two 25,000 bbl/day (barrels/day) plants due to come on-stream by 1988 (Pitman 1981).

Oil is extracted from shale by retorting it at about 500°C to break down the kerogen which nature has neglected to do. This cannot yet be done at prices competitive with present OPEC oil, but trials are in progress in both the USA and Australia to find new and cheaper methods for their own considerable oil shale reserves. Resources are huge; Skinner (1976, p. 35 *et seq.*) suggests that energy locked in shales is equivalent to at least $10^{26}$ joules, although he also points out that only a small part of it is recoverable. Even so, a mere 1 per cent of that potential would yield $10^{24}$J, more than the energy contained in oil, gas, and tar sand combined.

### 7.3.1 Types of oil shale

There are two types of oil shale, torbanite, named after the Scottish type locality, and true oil shale.

*Torbanite.*   This essentially a bog-head, cannel or sapropelic coal formed from terrestrial materials, mainly plant matter, freshwater algae and spores. Estonian varieties yield over 300 litres of oil per tonne, South African ones, somewhat less; most others produce only 45–50 litre/tonne. As it needs the equivalent of 40 litres of oil to process one tonne of shale, a yield of 40 l/t is usually taken as the economic cut-off grade. Torbanitic kerogens generate alkanes and cycloalkanes when processed, in contrast to normal coals which give aromatics.

*True oil shales.*   These are also kerogen-rich, but were formed in shallow marine, lacustrine, or deltaic environments. The origin of the kerogen is obscure, but is probably largely terrestrial, humic and algaeic. Shales yield some 90 litres/tonne of oil or more; some varieties reach 250 l/t.

The Green River shales are probably the most studied of all oil shales. This Eocene formation covers 40,000 km² of Colorado, Utah and Wyoming in the USA. It is up to 600 m thick and averages 115 litres/tonne of oil with some parts yielding as much as 240 litres. Reserves of $2 \times 10^9$ bbl are estimated, but overburden may be up to 300 m thick. Skinner (1976) estimates the shales contain $0.75 \times 10^{22}$ J of energy, assuming that only half the rock grading over 40 l/t can be mined. Thirty other states in the USA also have workable shales.

The Rundle oil shale of Queensland in Australia has a similar potential of $2 \times 10^9$ bbl, more than all the oil in the North Sea Forties field: a second field of equal size has also been found in Queensland and several others show promise (Pitman 1981). Rundle yields about 90 l/t but, because it gives up its oil more readily than do the Green River shales, potential costs are lower. Recent falls in oil price, however, have cut development plans.

The United Kingdom also has potential for shale oil. In addition to the small Carboniferous torbanite field in Scotland, there are extensive Jurassic oil shales in the Kimmeridge Clay which stretches from Dorset to the Wash and into Cleveland (Fig. 7.10). Twenty one million tonnes of oil shale have been proved in Dorset alone and the potential is good elsewhere. It is largely ignored at present in favour of more easily won onshore oil, such as at Wytch Farm, Dorset.

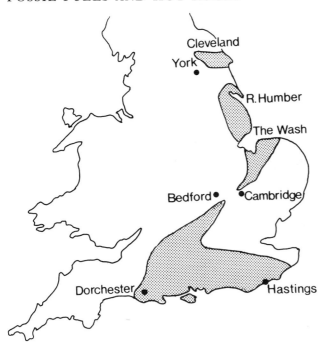

**Figure 7.10**
General extent of the Kimmeridge Clay in Britain.

### 7.3.2 Processing

Torbanite and oil shales are shallow-water rocks whose kerogen is formed largely from terrestrial matter. Presumably, they were not buried deeply enough or heated sufficiently to reduce the kerogen to oily substances. To produce oil, the kerogen must therefore be broken down artificially. This is done by retorting at 500°C to yield a heavy aromatic oil, which, because it is too viscous to pipe when cold, must be cracked on site to lighter hydrocarbons before refining. Fuel for heating is no problem; the shale is its own fuel. However, the oil-depleted shale remaining is a problem. Retorting bloats it, so that it takes up 30 per cent more space than it did beforehand, which means it cannot all be returned to its former site. This is just one of many environmental problems associated with oil shale.

Underground retorting may solve some difficulties. Trials have been carried out in both the USA and Australia to form underground retorts within the shale by fragmenting the rock in place by blasting and then firing it (Fig. 7.11). The oil percolates downwards and is collected in a gallery below the retort level and taken to the surface for cracking and hydrogenation to alkanes.

Present oil prices still do not encourage shale oil production, except in a few otherwise oil-poor countries, but shales will certainly be exploited when traditional oil sources run out. They provide the same oils and similar petrochemicals as traditional crudes, with a slight additional bonus of ammonia, sodium bicarbonate, alumina, and sulphur as by-products. Price rises in liquid crudes could even swing production in favour of syncrudes earlier.

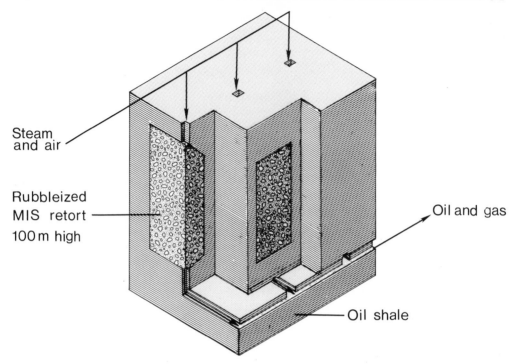

Steam
and air

Rubbleized
MIS retort
100 m high

Oil and gas

Oil shale

**Figure 7.11**  Block diagram of MIS (modified *in situ*) retorts formed by 'rubbleizing' the oil shale by blasting. The rubble is ignited at the top, and air and steam injected; the combustion-retorting zone burns downwards at between 900 and 1000°C. Oils and gases condense below the retorting zone and percolate into the lower gallery where they are collected and pumped to the surface at about 70°C for refining.

### 7.3.3  Oil from coal

Oil can also be retorted from bituminous coals. Good coals may yield as much as 450 litres/tonne, poorer coals produce less, but oil extraction may be a more economically suitable use for them. Germany obtained much of its petroleum from coal during World War II, and South Africa does today. To plan for the future, British Coal is now installing a pilot plant to produce petroleum at the Point of Air colliery in North Wales. This is a most welcome and imaginative project which may well cushion the effect of the loss of oil as the North Sea oil fields decline.

## 7.4  Coal

Wherever coal crops out it has probably been used for millenia as a local fuel. Sea coal, shipped to London from northern England in the 11th century, was an early attempt at wider distribution, but it was Abraham Darby who, in 1709, first used coal industrially when he proved that iron could be smelted by coked coal instead of charcoal. Industry developed where coal and iron ore occurred together, but the transport of bulk raw materials remained a problem in Britain until the development of the canal system in the mid-18th and the railways in the mid-19th centuries. Since 1709, coal has become a widely used industrial fuel and, for a long time, it was the only fuel. Early in the last century coal gas became important too, not only in industry, but for street lighting and for domestic lighting and cooking. By 1850, coal-tar chemicals had been found to be useful by-products.

Coal was paramount as fuel until well into this century; oil then began to usurp it. Steam ships found oil easier, quicker, and cleaner to bunker, and it simplified stoking. On the railways, steam locomotives were replaced by diesel and electric engines, and many power stations changed from coal to oil. Coal gas has now been supplanted by natural petroleum gas and coal-tars have lost ground to petrochemicals. Despite such competition, world coal production (although not British production) has continued to grow as the need for energy has increased. Coal has the final advantage, for its resources far outweigh those of all the other fossil and nuclear fuels combined, and have been variously estimated at 200–300 years supply. Bender (1982) quotes world fuel resources as:

| | |
|---|---|
| Coal | $10,125 \times 10^9$ tons |
| Tar sands and oil shale | $1080 \times 10^9$ tons coal equivalent |
| Oil | $647 \times 10^9$ tons coal equivalent |
| Nuclear fuels* | $+ 200 \times 10^9$ tons coal equivalent |

Coal will once again become a leading fuel as other fuels are depleted. Britain is well supplied with coal, but it is deep and the seams are generally thin. Good coals occur in other countries too (Figure 7.13), often in seams many metres thick, under thin cover, and much easier to mine. Many of the world's best coals are Carboniferous, but coal occurs in rocks of many ages, from the Devonian upwards. Devonian coals, however, are rare (there is one small field on Bear Island, USSR). A number of coalfields are Mesozoic; Saxonvale in New South Wales is an example. There, the seams are 20 m thick with reserves of a billion tonnes (Gomez 1985). Over half the world's coalfields are Tertiary (Johnson 1981). Tertiary coal occurs in Colombia and a recently opened strip mine is working Palaeocene coal in seams 10 m thick with reserves of sixteen billion tonnes (Burger 1985). Such coals sell at a fraction of the cost of British deep mined coal.

### 7.4.1 Origin of coal

Like oil, coal is a product of the anaerobic decay of plant material, but in this case the plants are entirely land flora. Humic coals are formed from leaves, stems, bark and wood; sapropelic coals from spores, pollens and algae. Sapropelic coals are cannels, bogheads and torbanites and were discussed under oil shales. Here we are concerned only with the humic type.

Coalfields formed where plant debris accumulated thickly over a wide area. Warm, humid swamps were the ideal environment and were either paralic

*(from ores workable at \$130/kg uranium: much greater resources are available if prices rise).

marine swamps formed under lagoonal, littoral and deltaic conditions, or limnic swamps associated with freshwater inland basins. A few coals, as in southern Africa, were formed in seasonal swamps at the end of a glaciation.

Plant debris forms peat in swamps where acid waters and lack of oxygen prevent normal decay. Anaerobic bacteria break plant material down, expelling oxygen and nitrogen. Soluble products are removed in the moisture squeezed out by pressure as more material is deposited above. Elements are lost, with a consequent relative increase in carbon content in the form of resins, lignin and waxes. Peat is the first product of the bacterial decay and retains fibrous structures and easily recognizable plant remains. During periods of coastal sinking, the peat is buried by muds and sands. If sinking pauses, more peat is formed; as sinking resumes, new sediment is laid down. Eventually a succession of peat beds separated by sedimentary material is built up. As the peat is buried and comes under increasing pressure and rising temperature, diagenetic changes occur; more moisture and more volatiles are lost, and bulk is reduced to a fifth of its original volume to form brown çoal or lignite, roughly synonymous terms. Lignite is a soft brown to black crumbly fuel which still retains some recognizable plant remains. It burns with a pungent heavy yellow smoke which covers cities which rely on it, with a pall of sulphurous winter-time smog; Ankara in Turkey is a classic example. As burial increases, so does rank, and sub-bituminous coal is formed by a further

**Table 7.1**  Comparison of coals.

| | Compaction factor: assuming 10 m of original peat | Volatiles % | Carbon % | Energy j/kg | Uses |
|---|---|---|---|---|---|
| Peat | 10 m | | | $25 \times 10^6$ | Domestic, small-scale industry |
| | | 55 | 60 | | |
| Lignite and brown coals | | | | $30 \times 10^6$ | Domestic and industrial |
| | 2 m | 40 | 70 | | |
| Sub-bituminous coals | | | | | Domestic and general usage |
| | 1 m | | 80 | | |
| Low rank bituminous coals | | 30 | | $35 \times 10^6$ | Domestic and general usage |
| High rank bituminous coals (coking) | | | | | |
| | 1 m | 20 | (82–89) | | Coking coals |
| High rank bituminous coals (steam) | | | | | |
| | | | | | Steam coals |
| Anthracite | 1 m | 10 | 90 | $38 \times 10^6$ | Smokeless fuels |
| | | 0 | 95 | | |

rise in carbon and a fall in volatile content. Sub-bituminous coals are general household coals, hard, brittle, shiny and black, now compressed to only 10 per cent of the original peat they were formed from. They are the commonest of all proper coals but they do not coke.

Rank increases as carbon content increases and volatiles are lost. Sub-bituminous pass into bituminous coals. Low-rank bituminous coals are used for gas and general purposes, higher ranks for coke or for steam coals. Anthracite is the highest rank with 95 per cent carbon and less than 5 per cent volatiles. Anthracites were probably formed by high temperatures due to folding, thermal metamorphism, or depth of burial. South African anthracites are coals which were thermally metamorphosed by dolerites intruding the Karroo Supergroup; even coke and graphite were formed in some places (Johnson 1981).

Coal is not homogeneous, but is composed of bands with different characteristics related to changes in type of plant material during accumulation. Shiny clarain bands, formed from the woody materials, are separated by thin layers of dull, dark durain derived from finer debris, such as spores, resins and cuticles. Fusain, in thin sooty partings which soil the fingers, occurs too; it is formed from plant material which has lost all volatile matter. In addition to carbon and volatiles, coal contains sulphur, mostly as pyrite, and 5–10 per cent hydrogen. It also contains mineral matter washed into the swamp, which forms the ash left after burning.

The peat we see in Scotland and Ireland is not in a coal-forming environment. It is blanket peat, formed on the landsurface, and most unlikely ever to be preserved by burial. Nevertheless, it has its uses; it is used as a domestic fuel and in Ireland is mined for power generation. Scottish peat is especially important to the whisky industry! It adds flavour during manufacture. The peat now forming in the extensive swamps of the Ganges delta is much more akin to the coal-forming peat of the past.

### 7.4.2 Coal sedimentology

Coals occur in sequences of sandy, silty and shaley rocks formed in either paralic or limnic environments. Paralic coals are formed on regionally sinking continental margins associated with occasional marine transgressions, now represented by shaley marine bands within otherwise deltaic, lagoonal, and generally terrestrial sedimentary rocks. British coals are paralic and Figure 7.12 shows a typical coal-bearing sequence from the British Carboniferous. Each upward-coarsening cycle (or cyclothem) represents the restoration of very shallow water conditions in which peat could form following flooding with, in some cases, marine transgression.

Limnic coals formed in sinking inland basins. They occur with sedimentary rocks of terrestrial origin derived from the erosion of nearby mountains. These rocks are typically coarser than those in paralic cyclothems and include conglomerates and coarse reddish arkoses in addition to shales and siltstones, but they include no marine bands. The coals developed on the margins of lakes or on the surfaces of alluvial fans. The Transvaal Karroo coals, formed close in time and place to glaciation, have similar limnic associations, as do coals in Brazil and Australia.

Environment

| | | |
|---|---|---|
| Coal | | swamp |
| Sandstone | | delta |
| Silty mudstone | | lagoon |
| Marine shell band | | marine |
| Coal | | swamp |
| Siltstone | | delta |
| Mudstone with ironstone band | | |
| Coal | | swamp |
| Sandstone and siltstone | | delta |
| Coal with shale bands | | swamp |

**Figure 7.12**
Typical sequence in the British Carboniferous.
(From *The Earth's Physical Resources — Block 2: Energy Resources*. Open University S-26 1973, with permission.)

## 7.4.3 Distribution of coal

Coal is widely distributed and is known on every continent, including Antarctica. Countries which lack coal are mainly those with large tracts of Precambrian and Lower Palaeozoic rocks, such as those in Central Africa, for coal could not form until land plants had evolved, but even Tanzania has some coal in the Permo-Carboniferous Karroo rocks in the extreme south. North Africa and Arabia are also less fortunate in coal than many other regions, but at least they have oil to console them. Figure 7.13 shows the world-wide distribution of coalfields.

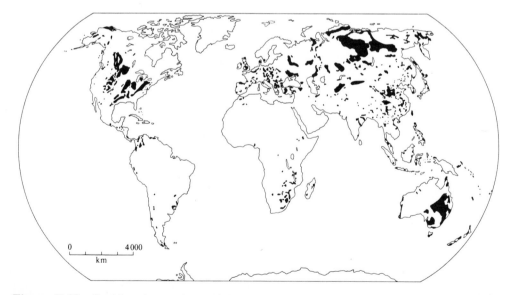

0        4000
km

**Figure 7.13**   Coal-bearing regions of the world.
(From Brown and Skipsey 1986, with permission)

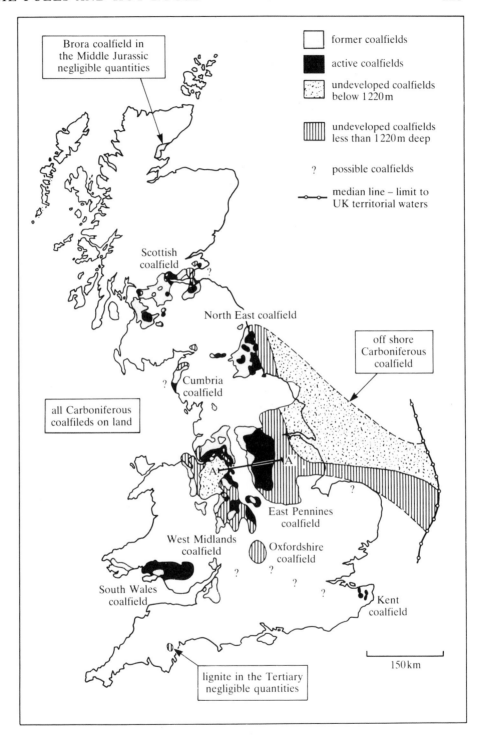

**Figure 7.14** The location of the British coalfields and their offshore extension in the southern North Sea.

(From Brown and Skipsey 1986, with permission)

*Coal in Britain*.    Britain is fortunate in having huge coal resources, but less so in that most of it is deep, the seams thin, and the coal-bearing formations often folded and strongly faulted. Except for a small Jurassic field in Scotland and Oligocene lignites in Devon, all British coals are Carboniferous (Fig. 7.14). Figure 7.15 shows where the coal-forming swamps lay and Figure 7.16 is a typical cross-section through a British coalfield, with concealed coal to the east.

The British Carboniferous commences with a basal conglomerate resting on the Old Red Sandstone surface. Above the conglomerate is the (Dinantian) Carboniferous Limestone followed by the (Namurian) Millstone Grit Series; the (Wesphalian) Coal Measures complete the sequence. The age of coal-bearing strata, however, changes from Scotland southwards. In Scotland and northernmost England coal occurs below the Millstone Grit, and the underlying limestones are thin. Southwards, in Yorkshire, the Carboniferous Limestone thickens and the coal is confined to the Coal Measures proper, above the Millstone Grit. Lower, Middle and Upper Coal Measures are recognized, but not all are productive in every coalfield. In Lancashire, only the Lower and Middle Coal Measures are coal-bearing, with the Upper Coal Measures barren and poorly represented. In South Wales, on the other hand the whole sequence is coal-bearing.

Coal Measure rocks consist of shales, siltstones, and sandstones, with occasional limestones. Shales containing marine fossils, including goniatites and brachiopods, form marine bands and indicate short-lived marine incursions. Coals are variable in quality and few seams reach two metres in thickness. The British Coal corporation considers seams thinner than 0.6 m as unsuitable for machine mining and uses that figure as its basis for reserve estimates, although a few decades ago 0.3 m (12 inch) seams were hand-mined. In general, British coals are good bituminous coals and, in South Wales, rank increases westwards to

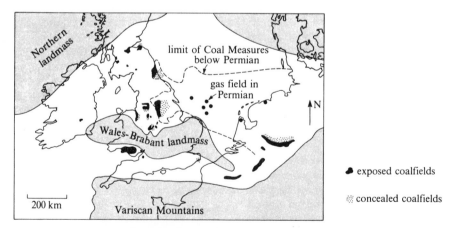

**Figure 7.15**    The distribution of the coalfields of north-west Europe, together with the area of the southern North Sea underlain by Coal Measures. This vast area was originally covered by Carboniferous deltas which originated from the Northern landmass. The Wales – Brabant landmass persisted as a land area throughout most of the Upper Carboniferous, separating the northern and southern deltaic provinces.

(From Brown and Skipsey 1986, with permission)

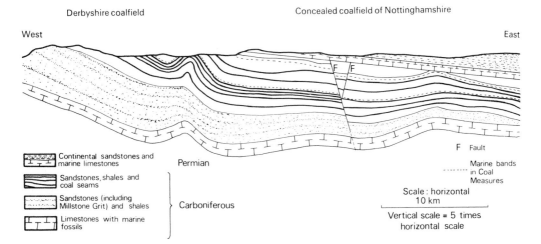

**Figure 7.16**  A geological section through the East Pennine coalfield, i.e. the Yorkshire, Derbyshire and Nottinghamshire fields, UK.
(From *The Earth's Physical Resources — Block 2: Energy Resources*. Open University S-26 1973. Crown copyright: with permission).

culminate in valuable anthracites. Several explanations have been given for this. The simplest is that heat from an unseen intrusion below drove off the volatiles, although there is only indirect evidence for such an intrusion (Bloxam and Owen 1985). Another theory is that heating was due to the load imposed by another 2500 m of Coal Measures which has now been eroded away. Trotter (1948), however, suggested that the heating was caused by friction resulting from thrusting along the Careg Cennen Disturbance.

Coals lie on a seat-earth of fire-clay, a material rich in silica and alumina but poor in iron and alkalies, which represents what were the soils first colonized by the coal-forming plants. As its name implies, fire-clay is useful for making refractory bricks, although it now has to compete with serpentinous by-products from chrome mining (see section 8.7.1). Thin clay ironstone beds also occur in the Coal Measures and were once important iron ores although, in these days of mass mining, they are valueless.

The literature on British coalfields is copious and those wishing to study it further, should refer especially to the publications of the British Geological Survey.

*North American Coalfields.*    North American coals occur in both the USA and in Canada. They include a few small areas of anthracite, abundant bituminous coals, and large areas of sub-bituminous coals and lignite. North America contains 27 per cent of the worlds coal resources (calculated from Averitt 1973). The distribution of coals in North America (excluding Alaska) is shown in Figure 7.17.

The figure shows that they occur in three main groups: the Appalachian fields in the east, the Interior fields further westwards, and the Rocky Mountain fields in the west. The Appalachian fields cover parts of Pennsylvania, Ohio, West Virginia, Virginia, Maryland, Kentucky, Tennessee, Alabama and Georgia. The

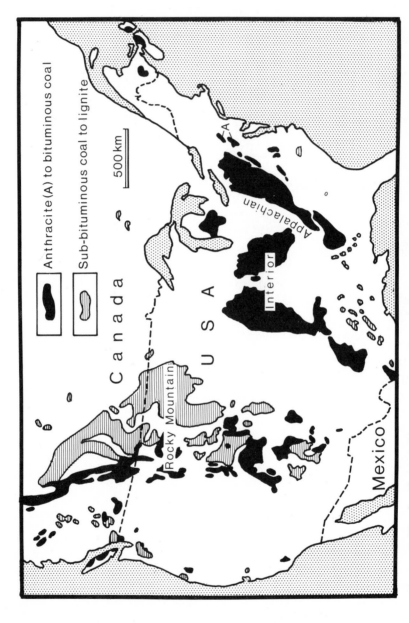

**Figure 7.17** Coalfields in North America. The Appalachian and Interior fields are Carboniferous, and mainly bituminous coals, with some anthracite. The Rocky Mountain fields are Cretaceous, with bituminous and sub-bituminous coals, and lignites. Some Tertiary coals occur in Alaska. (Adapted from Dietrich and Skinner, 1979)

coals are predominantly Upper Carboniferous (Pennsylvanian) with a few in the Lower Carboniferous (Mississippian). In the eastern region they were strongly folded during the Appalachian orogeny, in the western region, less so. The coals are bituminous and tend to increase in rank eastwards, with a few small anthracite fields in the extreme northeast. The main areas of mining activity are in the states of Pennsylvania and Ohio where dips are gentle, and the coal measures often form the tops of hills where they can be strip mined.

The thickness of the Pennsylvanian coal seams in the northern parts of the Appalachian region is usually less than three metres but one notable seam, the Mammoth, which occurs in Pennsylvania, is 15–18 m thick. Seams in the southern Applachian coal fields are thinner, mostly less than two metres thick. These latter coals are close to the Clinton iron ores and were the reason why the steel industry was originally developed at Birmingham, Alabama.

The Interior coal fields are to the west of the Applachian fields. The coals are again Pennsylvanian in age and, they are again, bituminous. The fields stretch from Texas, through Oklahoma, Kansas, Missouri and Kentucky, to Indiana, Illinois, and into Michigan.

The Rocky Mountain fields are mainly Upper Cretaceous. They extend northwards from New Mexico and Arizona, as far as Montana and the Dakotas, and over the border into Canada, occurring in Alberta, British Columbia and Saskatchewan. There are even some small deposits in the Yukon. The western parts of this huge coal province contain bituminous coals with some sub-bituminous, and locally, small areas of anthracite related to igneous intrusions. The eastern fields contain mainly sub-bituminous coals and lignites. The Rocky Mountain areas have some of the thickest seams in North America. One seam in Wyoming is 25 m thick and seams up to 50 m thick have been intersected in boreholes in Montana (Jensen and Bateman 1979).

Small fields of Tertiary coal are found sporadically along the Pacific costal region, more abundantly in British Columbia than in the USA. Bituminous, sub-bituminous and lignitic coals occur. Tertiary coals also occur in Alaska, but they are difficult to work owing to structural problems; some are mined for domestic use.

*Some other coalfields.*    Many countries are major exporters of coal. They include Canada, the USA and the Republic of South Africa. Australia, Brazil, and Columbia are also exporters. These countries have the advantage of huge deposits with gently dipping outcropping seams many metres thick. Britain may boast it produces the cheapest deep mined coal, but it cannot match the costs of these massive open-cast producers.

Figure 7.13 shows the general distribution of the world's coalfields and it can be seen that they are surprisingly widely spread. Iran, for instance, is seldom thought of as a coal producer yet it has several small fields of good bituminous and coking coal of Rhaetic-Liassic age. The coals are limnic and the seams mostly thin. Turkey is more fortunate with both bituminous coal and lignites of Permian and younger ages and, at Zonguldak, 150 km east of Istanbul, there is an important Carboniferous field with seams up to 10 m thick extending under the Black Sea. The coal is of good metallurgical quality and the Turkish steel industry has been established nearby (Sarp 1961).

Many do not appreciate that India also has a flourishing coal industry; it is the fifth largest in the world. The coal is largely Permian and occurs mainly in Bengal, Bihar, and Hyderabad. Sixty six per cent of reserves are in seams 1.5–20 m thick, and nearly all mines are open-cast (White 1985). There are also small Tertiary lignite mines in the north-east and in the Himalayan foothills.

### 7.4.4 Prospecting for coal

Rocks likely to contain coal are relatively well known in the world. The search is therefore directed first towards identifying formations likely to contain coal, followed by pitting and drilling. In Britain, during the 1940s, a concerted search was made for coal that could be open-casted. The probable sub-outcrops of seams beneath deep drift were located and hand-drilled to about 25 m to confirm their position, then machine drilled to ensure a useful tonnage.

In Africa, the Ecca Division of the Karroo Supergroup are important coal-bearing rocks. In Uganda the several small areas of Karroo which contained Ecca rocks were drilled down to the Precambrian rocks below. Only coaly partings about 2 mm thick were found, and it could be confidently stated that no workable coal occurred for there were no other rocks likely to contain it (Barnes 1961, p. 67). Tanzania is more fortunate and does have Karroo-age seams. Malawi too, has now found workable Karroo coal and is no longer dependent on imports. South Africa mines Karroo coal extensively.

In many countries, Britain included, all outcropping coalfields have been discovered and the search is now for concealed fields which lie beneath unconformities or do not crop out for other reasons. Some may even lie beneath sea floors. Such searches rely on a combination of structural interpretation, stratigraphy, sedimentology and deep drilling, helped by geophysical investigations. British Coal has had particular success with seismic reflection methods in exploring the concealed north-east Leicestershire and Warwickshire fields. Even in established coalfields, coal may exist which has not been mined for technical reasons, sometimes because seams are too thin for modern mechanized mining, or because they continue below feasible mining depth. British Coal considers seams deeper than 1200 m as now unmineable, but a time may come when such coal can be extracted, possibly by remotely-controlled mining or by underground gasification.

## 7.5  Geothermal energy

Geothermal energy is the term used to describe energy produced by tapping the natural heat of the earth. Hot springs are the usual source, but attempts are now being made to extract heat from great depths by injecting water into artificially fractured hot rocks and retrieving it at elevated temperatures. The use of hot springs is not new. The Romans, and later the Turks sited bath houses at hot springs and such Turkish baths still exist in Turkey today. Hot springs were first used for power generation at Lardarello in northern Italy in 1904. Iceland and New Zealand followed suit in the 1920s. Today, many countries use geothermally-produced power, the USA and the Philippines being the leaders in the amount generated.

**Figure 7.18**   Nightingale Springs geothermal power station, Nevada, USA.

### 7.5.1  Types of hot spring

Hot springs are associated with volcanic activity, usually in its dying stages. Springs may produce dry steam, wet steam, or hot water, and all can be used, although in different ways.

*Dry steam springs.*   Dry steam springs provide high temperature steam at moderate pressure. The steam can be led directly to turbines to generate power. It then condenses to pure water which can be used for a number of purposes, or allowed to drain into rivers after cooling. Larderello was the earliest dry steam area exploited. Nevada, New Mexico and California also use dry steam. (Fig. 7.17).

*Wet steam springs.*   Wet steam springs are about twenty times more common than dry steam springs. They contain superheated water confined under considerable pressure below ground. When a reservoir is tapped, pressure is relieved. As the water reaches the surface 10–20 per cent flashes to steam in a mixture of steam and boiling water. The steam can be used directly for power generation and condenses to pure water, but the original water is laden with dissolved salts and pollutes any rivers it drains into. New Zealand and Iceland have this type of spring.

*Hot water springs.*   Hot water springs are common and were once thought to be industrially useless. Now, those with temperatures above $50°C$ have a number of applications. Domestic and industrial heating is the main use, and USSR calculates that it saves itself 15 million tonnes of conventional fuel each year by using hot springs to heat Siberian mines. New Zealand uses them for air-conditioning. Even power can be generated by vaporizing and condensing an intermediary fluid with a low boiling point, such as iso-butane ($C_4H_{10}$), in a closed circuit.

Hot water springs are mineral-rich and may pollute anything they drain into. Even pure hot water will pollute (by heat) and may even alter local ecology. A notable example was the growth of coral where the warm water from the old Battersea power station was emitted into the Thames, in London, UK.

### 7.5.2  Hot spring geology

Hot springs occur where ground water emerges at the surface after having passed through aquifers in volcanic areas, usually through leakage along faults. To be useful, hot water or steam must be confined in a reservoir so that it can be tapped. In some areas the reservoirs are very small and refill and discharge themselves at regular intervals in the form of geysers. Old Faithful in the Yellowstone National Park in Wyoming, USA, is an example, and emits an impressive fountain of steam and water every 25 minutes. To provide industrial power, reservoirs must be large enough to contain sufficient superheated water or steam to provide a continuous supply. Principles analogous to oil geology apply. Reservoirs are mainly anticlinal traps in porous rocks overlain by impermeable cap rocks. Unlike oil reservoirs, however, they are continually replenished by new supplies of steam or water. The reservoirs are smaller than oil reservoirs and must lie only a few hundred metres deep to be viable (Fig. 7.18).

Hot springs are found in volcanic areas and usually make their presence obvious by a pall of steam overhanging pools of hot water surrounded by tufas or sinters (Fig. 7.19). The most productive sites for tapping, however, may not be so obvious and may be some distance away from the springs. Thermal scanning from

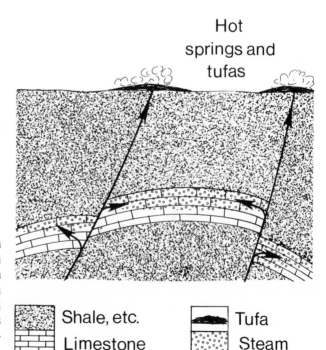

**Figure 7.19**
A geothermal reservoir. Steam rising on faults is collected in the limestone aquifer, which has a cap-rock of shale. In Turkey the succession is often flysch. Steam escaping up faults forms hot springs and calcareous tufas at the surface.

Shale, etc.

Limestone

Tufa

Steam

**Figure 7.20** Hot springs surrounded by travertine at West Thumb in the Yellowstone National Park, Wyoming, USA.

aircraft capable of detecting surface temperature differences of ¼ °C may indicate where reservoir rocks containing hot water and steam lie closest to the surface. Shallow drill holes can also be sunk and the temperature recorded in them so that isotherms can be plotted. Well holes can then be drilled.

Although geothermal energy may appear to be a cheap energy source, it is a limited source and seldom occurs just where it is wanted. Even so, Watson (1983, p. 25) says that Italy obtains 11 per cent of its energy in this way, although this does sound to this author a rather optimistic estimate. New Zealand only manages to obtain three per cent of its energy requirements from geothermal springs.

### 7.5.3 Hot rocks

Hot-rock technology is in its infancy. It is full of promise but whether it can fulfill that promise remains to be seen. The theory is attractive; find an area of high geothermal gradient, drill two boreholes about 100 m apart and fracture the ground between them at depth, then pump water down one hole and retrieve it from the other in the form of steam or superheated water. The first experiments have not been notably successful. Holes sunk 3 km to a granite in New Mexico heated water to only 115°C when retrieved, although the granite was at 190°. In Cornwall, UK, test drilling of two holes in granite 80 m apart is in progress so that fracturing methods can be tested to connect them at the bottom by a permeable

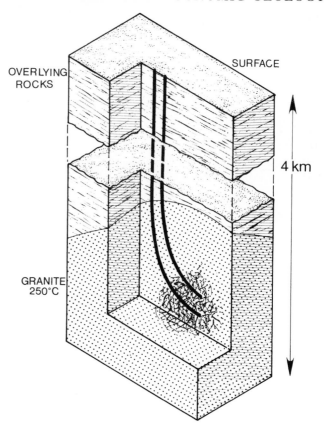

**Figure 7.21**
Hot-rock energy. Two wells are sunk 80–100 m apart into granite, and at the bottom the ground is fractured between them. Water pumped down one well is heated in the fractured zone and returns to the surface via the second well.

zone. Eventually it is hoped to retrieve the water pumped down at about 200°C to yield 50 MW. However, rocks have a poor heat-flow and heat taken out of the ground will cool the rocks in the immediate vicinity of the wells without appreciable regeneration, giving a life to each site of only about 20 years.

There is also a considerable reserve of energy — low enthalpy energy — in sedimentary basins. Aquifers at depth contain waters heated by the geothermal gradient to between 60° and 100°C. They can be tapped by drilling and used in a way similar to hot spring waters. Britain has a number of potential basins suitable for exploitations and some other countries have already tapped such sources.

## 7.6 Résumé

Energy is the key to industry, and without it a country cannot develop. Those countries which have coal and oil are fortunate; those that have not must look for other sources of power. Synfuels are one alternative but they have not yet come into their own except on a minor basis. Uranium is currently unpopular owing to problems of waste disposal, further aggravated by the Chernobyl disaster in Russia in 1986. Declining reserves of traditional liquid fuels may eventually force the issue here. Geothermal energy has promise, especially from hot rocks and low enthalpy sources, but is probably insufficient for total needs. There are also non-geological sources of energy. Hydroelectric power is favoured by environmentalists as clean and safe. However, its safety record is by no means perfect; at least 6000 people have died from dam failures this century, 2000 in one night at Vajont in Italy, only two decades ago. Nor is every country favoured with suitable mountains or suitable rainfall, Britain among them.

Tidal, wind and solar energy may plug some of the energy gap in the future, but fossil fuels still have a long way to run if oil shales and tar sands are counted, not to mention coal which has at least another century of life left to it. We must also remember that, without fossil fuels, we shall also be without the petrochemical by-products which are so essential to out present-day comfort.

# CHAPTER 8

# Industrial minerals

'Industrial minerals' is a convenient term to describe those unsung non-metallic minerals which support every aspect of our domestic economy. Until recently, geologists have found them uninteresting and students have not been encouraged by university courses, which tend to ignore such mundane materials. Owing to shortages of supplies from traditional sources, geologists have now been forced to take a more active, if reluctant, interest in them but, because they know little of industrial processes, they often fail to recognize the industrial potential of many of the mineral materials they see in the field.

Industrial minerals are difficult to classify, for many have multiple uses. Gypsum, for instance, is used in plasters, blackboard 'chalk', textiles, brewing waters, and alabaster ornaments, as well as for desalinating soils, diluting colliery dusts and regulating the setting time of cements. It is also used in paper and rubber manufacture, for polishing plate glass, in paints, and as a flux for smelting nickel ores; and these are by no means all its uses.

Only a representative selection of minerals will be considered here, and the emphasis will be on the usages of minerals, rather than on their occurrence, that is, this chapter is more about industrial mineralogy than industrial geology, for without a knowledge of what specific minerals are used for, geologists are unlikely to know which ones are useful and in what form, grade, and purity. Discoloured barite, for instance, is quite suitable for drilling muds, but not for paper making nor for refining sugar. A knowledge of geological occurrence is obviously useful, but that can be acquired later and to describe occurrences would make this book half as long again. At this stage, usage is more important than occurrence. Those wishing to know more about occurrence are recommended to read the excellent book, *Geology of the non-metallics*, by Harben and Bates (1984).

## 8.1 Construction and building industry

A wide range of geological products are used in construction and building, ranging from raw crushed stone to processed cements and plasters. Many constructional materials are bulky and low-priced and cannot be transported far from their source; they must occur close to where they are needed. Others, such as plasters and cements, are more compact and more expensive, and can even be exported profitably.

### 8.1.1 Dimension stone

Rock, squared off by masons for building blocks, is called dimension stone. More than 4000 years ago the Egyptians were using 2.5–tonne limestone blocks to build the Great Pyramids; they roofed the King's chamber with 50–tonne granite slabs (Edwards 1947, p. 265). In Europe, stone has been used for building since before Roman times and later, in Britain, freeholders were once entitled to quarry stone free from common land to build their houses. Now, however, many buildings which appear to be built of stone are really made of steel and concrete faced (clad) with stone slabs. Many buildings are clad with polished stone, and much geology can be learnt even in cities by examining them; one 300 m stretch of Swansea High Street has nine different polished stones, ranging from red and grey granites, through diorite, to the blue-grey anorthoclase-rich laurvikite from Norway, with its schiller-like play of colours. The condition of dated tombstones in churchyards is an indication of how well, or badly, various rocks stand industrial atmospheres. Indoors, polished serpentine marble may grace the walls of public hallways but outside, carbonate rocks do not stand up so well to pollution, as shown by the atmospherically-defaced gargoyles which glare down on us from the eaves of many cathedrals.

Statuary marble is not a dimension stone but it is convenient to consider it here. It is a fine-grained white marble from which large unfissured blocks can be quarried intact. Carrara in Italy has long been a traditional source; Michelangelo personally visited the quarries to select the blocks he wished to work with. Marble is still worked there today and choice blocks can cost up to £170 ($US 280) per tonne (1985).

### 8.1.2 Aggregates and ballasts

Aggregates are rock fragments graded to specific particle sizes. Some are mixed with cement to give body and strength to concrete. The best concrete aggregates are a mixture of sand and gravel. Sands and gravels may be available in mature river valleys, such as the Thames, where gravel pits can be seen in great numbers, many now exhausted and converted to recreational lakes. Some areas lack suitable gravel, so rock must be quarried and crushed instead. Standards for aggregates are laid down (by BSI in Britain): aggregates must not contain materials which might weaken the concrete or react with it, such as schists, pyrite or organic matter.

Roadstones are aggregates which are mixed with tar for road surfaces. They have specifications, too: if they are too hard, the road becomes polished and slippery, if too soft, it wears. Cohesive, medium-grained igneous rock such as dolerite, is ideal, but different rocks give different surfaces and one aggregate may be used on straight stretches of road, another on the bends. Overseas, many roads are not tarred. Volcanic ash often makes the best unsurfaced roads because it drains well, but in many tropical countries' roads are surfaced with red latritic earths (*murram*) of very variable serviceability, but it is often all that can be afforded or is available.

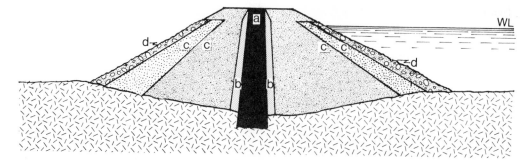

**Figure 8.1** A section through a major rock-fill dam. A core of impervious clay (a) is founded well into bedrock from which all weathered material has been removed. Sand filter beds (b) protect the core from erosion by water percolating within the main rock-fill (c–c). The main rock-fill is of medium grade aggregate covered by a layer of coarser broken rock. Rip-rap blocks, 1–2 m in size, protect the outer surface of the dam.

Ballast is crushed and sized rock used in construction to fill space and give weight. Ballast forms the upper part of railway road-beds to keep the sleepers in place. Specifications for ballasts may be lower than for concrete and roadstones, but still must meet some standards, even when used merely for rock-fill. In rock-fill dams — the most common type of dam — only a thin impermeable clay core-wall forms the actual barrier to the flow of water. This wall is supported on each side by permeable rock-fill ballast, laid with progressively coarser sizes outwards from the core (Fig. 8.1). Rip-rap of blocks as large as 1–2 m across, protect the exposed ballast surface.

### 8.1.3 Lightweight aggregates

Lightweight aggregates may be used in concretes where load-bearing strength can be sacrificed for lightness. Lightweight concrete floors in tower-block buildings save cost because the strength of the walls to support them can be reduced. Most lightweight aggregates are bloated rock fragments; i.e. they have been flash-heated so that pore-water contained in them turns instantaneously to steam, expanding the fragments to pumice-like material. Perlite, a glassy water-bearing form of rhyolite is often used for bloating, as is shale. Vermiculite, a form of chlorite, can also be bloated to form tiny concertina-like granules which contain so much air space that they can be laid loose in attics as a thermal insulant, or mixed with plaster to form sound-deadening walls.

### 8.1.4 Brick clays

The earliest bricks were made of sun-dried clay, with straw added for greater strength (a process still used in the Third World); but even kiln-fired bricks date back to Sumer in the 3rd millenium BC. Fired bricks can be made from a wide range of iron-bearing clays, providing they contain enough silt to prevent shrinkage and cracking on firing. The iron acts as a flux to assist fusion, and a little included carbonaceous matter helps burning. Different clays produce different bricks and different colours; there are specialized bricks for refractory use made from kaolin-rich clays and fire-clays.

## 8.2 Cements and plasters

The Sumerians used bitumen to cement their bricks together. By Roman times mortars were made by calcining limestone to lime (calcium oxide), hydrating it, and mixing it with sand. Then, the Romans found that by firing limestone mixed with volcanic ash (from Pozzuoli outside Naples) a stronger cement resulted which would set under water. Later clayey limestones were substituted for pozzolan raw materials and eventually, in about AD 1700, limestone and clay were mixed. In 1824, Joseph Aspdin found he could produce a better product by raising the calcining temperature to 1500°C and Portland cement, said to resemble Portland stone, was born. Even so, lime mortars and pozzolans are still used in many countries today.

### 8.2.1 Modern cements

Cement is now made by mixing crushed limestone with clay or shale and calcining them to a clinker. The clinker is then ground to a usable cement powder. Some limestones may be shaley, some clays calcareous, and constituents must be mixed in the proper proportions to provide the correct ratios of calcium, aluminium, and silica, together with some iron, to meet the specifications laid down by national standards. Too much iron in the raw materials gives an unpleasantly grey cement; excess phosphorus may cause concrete made with it to crack, (it is neutralized by adding fluorite); excess magnesia in a cement may also cause concrete to crack. A little magnesia, however, will make a slow-setting cement, suitable for mass structures such as dams. Cement sets by an exothermic reaction and the heat produced in a mass structure may cause it to expand and subsequently crack as it contracts on cooling. Slow-setting cements allow time for heat to be dissipated, often by brine circulated through pipes set into the concrete. Setting time can also be regulated by adding gypsum to the clinker.

In Britain, most cement is made from the Chalk or Carboniferous limestone. Other countries may use reef limestone or even coral reef itself, or shell-beds or travertines. Not every country is fortunate in having cement-making materials available. Uganda consists largely of Precambrian formations in which the few carbonate rocks are magnesium-rich. Mesozoic intrusive carbonate plugs (carbonatites) associated with alkaline volcanic complexes once seemed the only hope on which to base a cement industry. The variability of magnesia and the abundance of apatite and magnetite in the carbonatite caused continual problems, only partly solved by sweetening with Recent lake limestones later found in the Western Rift, 500 km away.

### 8.2.2 Plasters and other cements

Plasters are fine-textured, quick-setting cements which have little structural strength. Most are based on calcined gypsum, i.e. plaster of Paris which, when mixed with water, can be poured into a mould to give a sharp cast owing to a slight expansion on setting. Plaster of Paris is absorbent, and liquid clay slip poured into plaster moulds rapidly loses its water to the mould to produce ceramic slipware. Casts made of plaster are, of course, well-known for immobilizing broken limbs. Mixed with fine sand, plaster is used to give smooth finishes to walls and ceilings of buildings inside and as stucco outside, and, with other suitable binders, is used for wall- and plaster-boards and for pipe insulation.

There are many other cements and plasters. Parian and Keene's cements are both based on gypsum, mixed with borax or other mineral substances to give hard, almost glazed, finishes. Sorel's cement, made from calcined magnesite ($MgCO_3$) mixed with magnesium chloride, sets to a smooth, hard, warm resilient surface which can be waxed and polished; hospitals are often floored with it. Atomic cement is based on barite ($BaSO_4$) and used for X-ray and radiation screening.

### 8.3  Fillers, extenders, and dilutants

Fillers are inert substances used to bulk out manufactured materials — such as vinyl floorings, plastics, rubbers and paper — to give them weight and body, or to reduce their cost. In paper-making, they give both body and surface for, without the filler, the surface would be too porous to write on. Kaolin ($Al_2O_3.2SiO_2.2H_2O$) and talc ($3MgO.Si_4O_{10}.H_2O$) are the commonest paper fillers, but both have many other filler applications. They are used in recording discs, rubber, some soaps, and pencil leads. Kaolin, in particular, helps receptiveness to colour printing of textiles which contain it. Gypsum (*terra alba*) is another common filler used in printed textiles. Even diatomite ($SiO_2.nH_2O$) goes into textiles, papers and cardboards, but is perhaps better known as the *kieselguhr* used to absorb nitroglycerine in making dynamite. Where extra weight is needed, as in the heavy, glossy papers of the quality magazines, ground barite is used; barite is also mixed with asphalt as a non-sparking filler for the floors of explosives factories.

The cheapest filler of all is ground slate. Bound with shellac it once formed the basis of the old 78 r.p.m. gramophone records, but it has many applications where appearance can be sacrificed for cost. Car battery cases, roofing compounds, and industrial adhesives are examples.

The distinction between a filler and extender is fine; basically, a filler bulks out a solid substance, an extender thickens a fluid, such as paint. All the fillers mentioned can be used as extenders of paints, distempers, or emulsions. Paint is often extended with the clay mineral bentonite (sodium montmorillionite, — $(Al,Mg)_4Si_8O_{20}(OH)_4.nH_2O$) to give it thixotropic (non-drip) properties.

Dilutants dilute a chemically-active ingredient. Many medicinal pills are diluted with chalk i.e. calcium carbonate. An undiluted pill containing 50 mg of a drug would be very small, and difficult for a patient to handle. Bulked out with harmless chalk it is easier both to handle and for the chemist to dispense by volume. A less delicate application is the liberal spreading of gypsum dust in coal mines to reduce the concentration of highly combustible coal dust to below its explosive limit.

Carriers, are inert materials used to distribute active ingredients, such as insecticides, which have been absorbed onto them. Kaolin is a typical carrier used in crop dusting from aircraft.

The purpose of a drilling mud is to support the walls of deep boreholes during drilling and to counteract the pressure of inflowing oil, gas, and water. It also acts as a lubricant for the drill bit. Most are heavy muds based on suspensions of barite in water. Swelling muds contain bentonite; their purpose is to enter small cracks in the side of the well, swell, jellify, and seal them off.

Some minerals, notably kaolin, barite, and gypsum, have multiple uses as fillers, extenders, and dilutants. Despite its other name of 'china clay' — a reference to its original country of origin and not its use — the main market for kaolin is as a filler, extender and dilutant. Even so, kaolin is used in the ceramic industry, mainly as the principal constituent of ball clay. Kaolin is Britain's most important mineral export.

## 8.4 Abrasives

Abrasives are used in industry for shaping, finishing, cleaning and polishing products, or for preparing for another stage in the manufacturing process. They may be coarse or fine, hard or soft, depending on their purpose. Not all abrasives are industrial: some are used as domestic cleaners, or brass and silver polishes, even as toothpaste!

### 8.4.1 Hard natural abrasives

Diamond, corundum, emery and garnet are termed hard industrial abrasives. Diamond (crystalline carbon) is the hardest of all as No.10 in Mohs' scale of hardness. Its best-known industrial use is probably in diamond drill bits for rock drilling; bits may be armed with individually-set stones or with diamond-impregnated sintered metal. Diamonds are also used in stone-saws and grinding wheels, or powdered and suspended in vaseline as a polishing agent. Large stones may be drilled and used as dies through which wire is drawn, or as spinnerettes for a similar purpose in the production of artificial fibres. Boart, carbonado and ballas are names for different types of industrial diamonds.

Not all diamonds come from South Africa. USSR produces more carats, but South Africa yields more gems. Seventy per cent of all diamond production is in fact as industrial stones, and 70 per cent of all stones produced come from Africa; South Africa, Zaire, Botswana, Angola, Namibia, Ghana, Sierra Leone, and Tanzania are the more important producers. Australia has a huge recently-discovered potential of both industrial and gem quality. Natural industrial stones are, however, only a fifth of the market: man-made diamonds now dominate the industrial stone market.

Corundum is crystalline aluminium oxide ($Al_2O_3$) and, with a hardness of 9, second only to diamond. Although there are cheaper synthetic materials of equal hardness, such as carborundum, corundum is still superior because its parting gives chisel-like edges to its crushed grains which scrape away, rather than scratch, material being polished; it thus gives a finer finish (Harben and Bates

1984, p. 364). Corundum is found in silica-deficient pegmatites and contact metamorphic deposits.

Emery is a natural mixture of corundum and magnetite formed by the contact metasomatism of impure limestones and laterites. It was once a popular abrasive; the corundum cuts whilst the magnetite lubricates. Turkey and the Greek islands off the Turkish coast were the main producers, but synthetic abrasives have now destroyed the market.

Garnet has many varieties, but only almandine ($Fe_3Al_2Si_3O_{12}$) with a hardness of 8, is used industrially. High-quality cabinet makers' sand paper is really a garnet paper; garnet is also used to finish glass, dental instruments and even leather! Sandblasting, however, is one of its most important uses, for garnet grits are less likely to cause silicosis in the operator than silica sand; it is also heavier and harder than sand, so lasts longer and cuts better. Garnet is a by-product from beach placer mining of heavy mineral sands.

### 8.4.2 Silica abrasives

Silica is a cheap, commonly available abrasive with ahardnesss of 7; it is widely used in industry. Silica sand can be easily cleaned and sized, and is used for cheaper sand papers, in sand-blasting, and in many industrial metal polishes and scouring soaps. Diatomite has similar uses, mainly in scouring powders and polishes. Ground pumice is also used, especially in domestic scouring powders.

### 8.4.3 Soft abrasives

Dolomite is a typical soft abrasive. Mixed with paraffin it goes into metal polishes; it is also the abrasive in many toothpastes, and it forms the basis for final glass polishers and for scouring powders. Jewellers rouge (ground hematite) is a polish for precious metals and gemstones.

### 8.4.4 Synthetic abrasives

Carborundum — silicon carbide — is the oldest synthetic abrasive, but many more carbides, as well as nitrides, have now been developed, tailored to particular uses. Tungsten carbide is a well-known example. As noted above, even diamond has very successful competitors.

## 8.5  Fluxes

Fluxes are added to furnace charges during smelting to lower the reduction temperature, reduce the surface tension of the metal so that it will flow more easily, and to collect impurities into a fluid or crust-like slag which separates from the metal and floats on its surface. Some slags can be used to make rock wool or other by-products afterwards.

### 8.5.1 Carbonate fluxes

Limestone is a common flux; it is converted to calcium oxide in the furnace and then combines with silica to form calc-silicate slag, i.e.

$$CaO + SiO_2 \longrightarrow CaSiO_3$$

In iron smelting, the slag also picks up some manganese (a little is beneficial to the iron) and also sulphur, but not phosphorus. Some low-grade iron ores are only saleable because of their carbonate gangue and are sold as self-fluxing ores, bringing their own flux with them. Although not, perhaps, specifically a flux, many steel-making processes rely on dolomite basic linings to the hearth or converter. These linings are converted to calcium-magnesium oxide, which reacts with phosphorus pentoxide in the metal to form calcium and magnesium orthophosphates, purifying the iron. When discarded, the linings can be crushed and sold as basic slag fertilizers.

Limestone fluxes are used in many other extractive metallurgical processes, including the smelting of tin, lead, and mercury ores.

### 8.5.2 Silica fluxes

Silica fluxes are used in both copper and nickel smelting. They form iron silicate slags from the iron in chalcopyrite ($CuFeS_2$), bornite ($Cu_5FeS_4$), and pentlandite (($Fe.Ni)_9S_8$). The silica may be obtained from many sources; quartzite is typical. In one African copper mine, the oxidized ore zone consisted largely of granite gneiss richly impregnated with oxidized copper minerals. By using the gneiss as a silica flux to smelt the primary sulphide ore, they recovered the secondary copper for nothing.

### 8.5.3 Fluorite and cryolite

Demand for fluorite ($CaF_2$) or fluorspar, has outstripped supply in recent years. Fluorite removes silicon, sulphur, phosphorus and carbon from iron during steel making. To satisfy demand in Britain, tailings and waste dumps from abandoned lead mines were scavenged, and then the old mines themselves reworked. Any lead and zinc recovered became a by-product; a reversal of roles in the past when fluorite was the by-product. Fluorite also occurs without metallic ores in pegmatites and vein-like deposits, or as metasomatic replacements (Fig. 8.2).

More than half of all production of fluorite is for fluxes, although not all for steel; some is used to produce artificial cryolite. Cryolite ($Na_3AlF_6$) is a fluorine-bearing mineral once used as a combined electrolyte and flux in producing aluminium from its ores. The only source at Ivigtut in Greenland was exhausted by 1962. Cryolite is now manufactured from fluorite, sodium carbonate and aluminium hydroxide.

### 8.5.4 Borates

Borax, and borate minerals which can be converted to borax, occur in evaporite

**Figure 8.2**  An opencast working at the Kerio Fluorspar Company in the Rift Valley of Kenya.

deposits associated with volcanic activity. Turkey and USA, produce 90 per cent of world supplies between them. Borax is used to prevent oxidation in many processes where metals are melted, cast or joined, including welding. It is also used in glass making and in enamelling metals.

## 8.6  Pigments

Mineral pigments are used mainly in paints. Cadmium red, chrome and cadmium yellows, red lead, white lead and zinc white will be familiar names to most people. Antimonial sulphides and oxides are less well known: they are used in camouflage paints because they reflect infra-red radiation in the same way as foliage, so offering military vehicles protection from photo-reconnaissance aircaft. They are also used in flame-resisting fabrics. Mineral pigments, such as malachite green and antimonial black, were once prepared for their masters by the apprentices of the classical painters; some, including vermilion (the mercury mineral cinnabar), were in use as far back as the 7th millenium BC. Nowadays many industrial pigments are made from organic dyes, although some, such as ochres (limonite), umbers and siennas (iron-stained clays), continue to be mineral-based. Titania ($TiO_2$) and zinc carbonate are the basis for many white paints, titanium white having exceptional covering power. Burnt limestone and kaolin are still used for whitewashing walls in many countries.

Lead-based paints, however, are less popular now than in the past because of their toxic properties, and cadmium pigments are now also under suspicion. It has even been said that Napoleon's death was hastened by arsenical compounds used to stabilize the pigments in the wallpaper of his house on St Helena.

## 8.7 Ceramics

Ceramics consume a wide range of mineral products; building bricks were mentioned under constructional materials (section 8.1.4); dolomite furnace linings under fluxes (section 8.5.1). There are however, other types of refractories.

### 8.7.1 Industrial ceramics

Refractory bricks to survive temperatures of up to 1500°C can be made from fire-clays which form the seat-earths of coal seams. Fire-clays are highly kaolinitic (kaolin = $Al_4Si_4O_{10}(OH)_8$) and contain aluminium oxides. They can be shaped and fired in the same way as other bricks. Fire-clay, however, is now meeting increasing competition from other materials (Harben and Bates 1984, p. 92). Olivine with serpentine, and sub-grade chromite ore containing a high proportion of serpentine gangue, are the basis of a wide range of refractories used in metal-lurgical and other industries. Some refractories are made from artificial mullite by fusing kyanite or sillimanite, both forms of $Al_2SiO_5$, and both occur in schists and other metamorphosed clay-rocks.

Saggars, i.e. containers for firing ceramics in the pottery industry, are made of fire-clay, or from serpentine and kaolin (which gives a synthetic cordierite, $(Mg.Fe)_2Al_4Si_5O_{18}$). Other containers, such as crucibles for molten metals, are made from graphite (C), or from the more refractory zirconia ($ZrO_2$), made from zircon ($ZrSiO_4$) recovered as a by-product of beach placer mining.

### 8.7.2 Electrical insulants

Porcelain insulators were once a common sight on telephone poles and high tension power pylons. Now, glass is more usual but dielectric porcelain, made from kaolin, ground quartz and feldspar, is still used where heat may be involved, even in small domestic items, for it can be moulded into complicated shapes. Porcelain is also the insulant in sparking plugs, although for racing cars zirconia porcelain is used.

### 8.7.3 Domestic ceramics

In Britain, the pottery industry developed where both clay and coal occurred in the same area. Ball clay is found in North Staffordshire and the Potteries became famous under the influence of Wedgwood, Spode and Minton. Other districts in Britain, such as Swansea, were also once famous, but on a smaller scale and their industries failed to survive. Ball clay is a mixture of clay minerals, with kaolinite $(Al_4Si_4O_{10}(OH)_8)$ predominant, some fine silica and a little organic matter. It fires white, or nearly so. Most pottery districts produce sanitary ware, industrial ceramics and wall tiles in addition to fine china. From poorer clays they manufacture floor tiles and pipes.

Pottery clays are not used as mined. They are first mixed with ground silica (often flint) and feldspar to reduce shrinkage during firing. For the high quality bone china, phosphate is added in the form of bone ash. Porcelain is a generic, rather than a specific, term for various forms of fine-grained ceramics incorporating feldspar. Feldspar acts as a flux during firing and is also used in the glazes with which fired china is coated before being fired again to give an impervious vitrified surface. Feldspar also forms the glaze of enamelled iron mugs and plates called graniteware in some countries.

## 8.8 Glasses

Glass is a supercooled liquid, that is, it is a non-crystalline solid; but not all glasses are transparent. Most are made by melting silica with calcium oxide and soda or, sometimes, potash. A few per cent of lead oxide is included in soft crown glass to make it easier to mould, and barium may be added for brilliance. Lead content can be increased if the glass is to be decoratively cut and, in Britain, crystal glass must legally contain at least 30 per cent lead. Heat-resisting glasses, such as Pyrex or borosilicate glass, have borax added, but contain no lead. They are widely used for oven and chemical ware. Fluorite is used in optical glasses, and refractive index can be increased still further by adding lead. Very high refractive indices can be obtained with germanium oxide $(GeO_2)$ which, because of a similar molecular size, will substitute for silica $(SiO_2)$, molecule for molecule; fish eye camera lenses are examples of such glasses. Some glasses have lithia $(LiO_2)$ added to the melt to make it run more easily; for opacity, feldspar or arsenic is added to the melt. Colours are obtained from metal salts; cobalt for blue, selenium for red, uranium for amber.

Silica for glass-making must be free of iron-staining and is usually found as white quartz sands, although some optical glasses are made from vein quartz. Traces of selenium or manganese are added to the melt to remove small amounts of discolouration. Iron is used to colour brown and green bottle glasses so poorer quality sands can be used for them. Otherwise, all glass ingredients must be extremely pure, for even traces of metals may ruin a melt.

## 8.9 Electrical and electronic industries

Mineral commodities have many applications in the electrical industry. Insulating ceramics, such as porcelains, have already been mentioned (section 8.7.2). Where electrical insulation is needed in conjunction with very great heat, mica is used. Some minerals, such as quartz, have other special electrical properties.

**Figure 8.3**
A heating element for a domestic iron. The element is electrically insulated between two sheets of muscovite mica.

### 8.9.1 Micas

Many will be familiar with the heating elements in domestic irons used for pressing clothes; the incandescent heating element is sandwiched between two sheets of mica (Fig. 8.3). Muscovite ($KAl_2(Al,Si_3)O_{10}(OH,F)_2$) is the principal mica used, although phlogopite ($KMg_3(Al,Si_3)O_{10}(OH,F)_2$) has some applications too. Micas can be split into thin sheets and stamped to shape for commutators, condensers and transformer formers; even scrap can be ground, resin-bonded, and pressed to shape. Muscovite is sold in many commercial grades. The pink ruby mica is the most valuable and fetches several pounds sterling per kg for sheets the size of this page. Muscovite has many non-electrical uses, too, such as in peepholes and windows in furnaces and in reflective traffic paints. Biotite is used only as a filler.

### 8.9.2 Quartz

When subjected to an electrical field, quartz expands along one crystallographic axis and contracts on another, the piezo-electric effect. By cutting a thin plate from a crystal at a specific angle to the c-axis, the plate can be made to vibrate at a determined frequency, and so control emissions for clocks, transmitters, and for many other instruments which depend on oscillations. Mechanical strain on the crystal will produce the reverse effect, which also has applications. Piezo-electric quartz crystals must be free from inclusions and untwinned, or twinned on the dauphine law only. They are a high-value commodity, and the larger the crystal, the better the price. U.S. prices for 1986 quoted in the *Engineering and Mining Journal*, ranged from $2.50–$60.00/lb, depending on size and quality. The crystals occur in coarsely crystalline veins and pipes, or as large pebbles in streams. Brazil is the principal world supplier.

### 8.9.3 Electronic materials

A number of mineral products are used in solid state electronic devices. They include the metalloids silicon, selenium and germanium, and the metals gallium and indium. A recent advance is the substitution of gallium arsenide for silicon in chips. As the second most abundant element in the crust, supplies of silicon offer no problems; it is produced by reducing silica in a furnace in the presence of carbon. The other elements are much rarer. Selenium is recovered from blister copper during electrolytic refining. It is used in semi-conductors and has additional uses in light-sensitive equipment and as the coating on photocopier drums. Germanium, gallium and indium are all recovered from zinc (and some copper) smelter flue dusts. Germanium is also recovered from fly-ash from coal-fired power stations and, more rarely, from the rare sulphide minerals germanite $((Cu,Ge)(S,As))$ and argyrodite $(Ag_8GeS_6)$. Its electronic use is rapidly declining, and its main application now is the fibre optics and infra-red sensors.

Indium, like germanium, is also found in fly-ash. Its main electronic role is as a dopant for diode and transistor materials but it, too, has non-electronic uses, such as hardening aluminium and lead, and as a highly reflective backing for instrument mirrors. Gallium is another semi-conductor dopant. In addition to zinc smelter flue dusts, it also occurs in bauxite. Usage is largely electronic, but because it melts at 30° and boils at about 2100°C, whereas mercury boils at only 357°C, gallium makes an excellent fluid for high-temperature thermometers. Because it has excellent adhesion to glass, it is used in seals for high vacuum apparatus such as X-ray tubes; it is also used as a lubricant in space vehicles where other lubricants would vaporize.

## 8.10 Gemstones

The term gemstone covers both precious and semi-precious stones, that is, all minerals which are pleasing to look at when properly cut and polished. Precious stones are the rarer, semi-precious stones commoner and therefore cheaper to buy; any finer distinction runs into difficulty. Most gemstones are single crystals but a few are mineral aggregates, or are cryptocrystalline, such as opal and turquoise. Fewer still are organic; jet and amber are examples.

Cutting and polishing enhance the appearance of a natural stone but, sometimes a stone may not be all it seems. *Caveat emptor*, let the buyer beware! In doublets, only the top part is a gemstone, the bottom part is glass; coloured liquid may even fill a hollow between top and bottom to form a triplet (Fig. 8.4). Many minerals can be made to look attractive by good cutting if they form good crystals

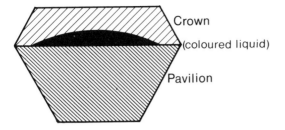

**Figure 8.4**
A false triplet gemstone with a crown (upper part) of quartz and a pavilion (lower part) of glass. Coloured liquid in the hollow of the crown adds colour.

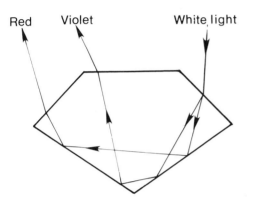

**Figure 8.5**
The path of light through a gemstone, showing dispersion and internal reflection.

and have poor cleavage (even diamond has a cleavage). A hardness greater than 5 helps, although both jet and amber are less than 3. Most gemstones are transparent, but not all; opal and moonstone are translucent, turquoise is opaque. In general, however, the higher the refractive index, dispersion and bire-fringence, the easier it is to produce the sparkle expected in most gemstones. As cutting must maximize these properties and give as many internal reflections as possible, a cutter must have an excellent knowledge of practical mineral optics to decide how he is to cut a stone to its best advantage (Fig. 8.5). Some cuts are complex, with over 80 facets (Fig. 8.6), but many semi-precious stones are merely well-cut coloured varieties of quartz and are cut more simply. Translucent and opaque stones are usually cut as cabochons with a smooth rounded surface to reflect light and colour to the best advantage.

### 8.10.1 Example of gemstones

*Diamonds* (C); H = 10; SG = 3.35; R.I. = 2.42; cubic octahedra. Found in kimberlite pipes and dykes, and in associated placers, both in rivers and offshore. Owing to their high R.I. they stand out from other colourless minerals if viewed under a thin cover of water in a prospecting pan; do not test their hardness with a hammer as some have done, they are brittle! Diamonds are valued by the 'Four Cs', colour, clarity, cut, carat.[*]

Zaire is by far the largest producer of diamonds, with an annual production

---

[*]Carat weight derives from the seeds of the carob tree; they have a very consistent weight and have been used for centuries as jeweller's weights in the eastern Mediterranean. The present metric carat is 200 mg.

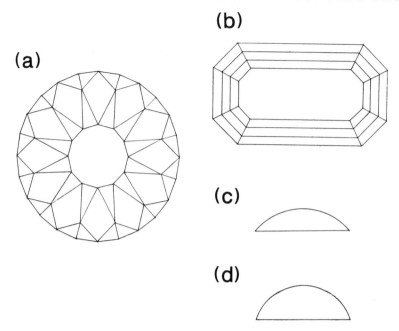

**Figure 8.6**   (a) The crown of an 86-facet brilliant-cut gemstone. The crown has 49 facets, the pavilion 37. (b) Crown of an emerald-cut stone. (c) Cross-section through a low-dome cabochon cut, used for oval stones. (d) Cross-section through a high-dome cabochon cut, used for round stones.

of 20 million metric carats (cts), of which only two percent are gem quality. Botswana and USSR are the second most important diamond producers at about 12 million cts each. South Africa ranks next, with 10 million cts, but because 48 per cent are gem stones, their total value is far greater than for any other country. Australia is now the fifth largest producer at 7 million cts, with 40 per cent cheap gem, and 5 per cent rare gem, quality. The remaining African diamond countries, and there are many, account for a mere 5 million cts between them. Brazil is the only sizeable non-African diamond producer (850,000 cts), but China has now entered the market with a small annual yield; production may well grow.

Taking world diamond production as a whole, gem quality averages about thirty per cent of the stones mined, most of which are sold through De Beer's Central Selling Organisation (the CSO). Some producers, including some in Zaire, now sell their stones independently, and Australia may very well do so in the future. The non-gem stones are sold as industrial diamonds, also through the CSO, but it should be noted that 80 per cent of all industrial stones used are now synthetic (section 8.4.1). Synthetic gem diamonds have yet to be made commercially.

*Beryl*   $(Be_2Al_2(Si_6O_{18}))$; H = 7.5 to 8; S.G. = 2.7; R.I. = 1.58; hexagonal. A good quality emerald, the green variety of beryl, is the most precious of all stones. Many emeralds, however, are not good quality and derive their looks by a clever setting which hides their defects. Acquamarine is a pale blue beryl, morganite, a pink to red variety, helidor, golden. Emeralds occur in pegmatites, contact meta-morphosed marbles and in mica-schists. Many of the best stones come from Colombia, but Pakistan, Zimbabwe and Zambia produce excellent stones, too.

*Corundum* ($Al_2O_3$); H = 9; S.G. = 4; R.I. = 1.76; hexagonal-trigonal. Corundum occurs in many silica-deficient igneous-associated rocks, including pegmatites, contact metasomatic deposits, and even in gneisses. Much production is from placer deposits, for it is an ideal placer mineral, moderately heavy, very hard and abrasion-resistant, with no cleavage. Ruby and sapphire are the gem varieties and compare with diamond and emerald in value. Some stones contain fine hair-like needles of rutile ($TiO_2$) which reflect light to cause asterism (a 3 or 6-pointed star of light). Star stones are cut as cabochons. Burma is the traditional source of rubies, but Pakistan, Afghanistan, Kenya and Tanzania also produce excellent stones. Sapphires come largely from Sri Lanka, Burma and Thailand. Rubies are red, but sapphires can be any colour, even colourless. In Britain, however, only blue sapphires appear to be acceptable. The colour of sapphire can be enhanced by heating, but the change is not always permanent.

Many other gems can be counted as precious, including chrysoberyl or alexandrite ($BeAl_2O_4$), not to be confused with beryl; topaz ($Al_2F_2SiO_4$), a dark yellow stone, although other colours also occur; and perhaps jades. Jades are of two types, the amphibole nephrite, and the pyroxene jadeite. Opal is also classed as precious and has many varieties, including fire opal, girasols, hyalite, and prasopal. Pearls, although precious, are too young geologically to be considered here.

### 8.10.2 Semi-precious stones

Many semi-precious stones are merely coloured varieties of quartz, cut and polished to bring out their best features. Examples are the purple amethyst, pink rose quartz, yellow citrine, smoky brown cairngorm, or even colourless rock crystal. Cryptocrystalline silica is also important, such as the white-speckled and red-speckled green plasma and heliotrope, green chrysoprase, and the banded agate and onyx. Even feldspar is used in jewellery as moonstone (orthoclase or albite), sunstone (adularia containing tiny flecks of haematite) and amazonstone of green microcline. Garnet provides a number of stones from the reddish varieties and, in Kenya, an emerald-green, chrome-bearing grossular garnet is called tsavoite from the Tsavo river, where it was found. Zoisites are stones which can be improved by heating. Pink zoisite, thulite, however is a long-established gem, and Tanzania recently discovered a blue zoisite, now named tanzanite.

Many other minerals are used in jewellery, even colourless cassiterite, the tin ore mineral, but a warning should be given that not every gemstone is what its name suggests, especially those prefixed by the epithet 'oriental'; oriental topaz, for instance, is cairngorm, otherwise known as smoky quartz. Any qualification of a gem name should give the buyer pause for thought. Garnet is sold under many names, including Cape ruby, Adelaid or Alabanda ruby, or even, for uvarovite, Ural emerald. *Caveat emptor* again!

### 8.10.3 Synthetic gemstones

Synthetic stones now form the bulk of the industrial diamond market; gemstones up to 1 carat have been manufactured too, but only at great expense, thus quite unprofitably. The same applies to emeralds: they can be made but the cost is prohibitive. Rubies and sapphires, on the other hand, have been manufactured since the 1890s in sizes up to 500 carats (100 g). They are difficult to distinguish from natural stones and some manufacturers seed them with the impurities found in natural stones, such as gallium, to make the task even harder; but a large part of production goes into watch and instrument bearings and the natural stone market still thrives.

Simulated diamonds have had some success. One form is a colourless yttrioaluminate garnet called YAG and, although dispersion and R.I. are lower than that of diamond, it can be coloured to give a series of pleasant stones. Titania, a synthetic rutile ($TiO_2$), actually exceeds the R.I. of diamond; fabulite ($SrTiO_3$) equals it; and the Watten diamond ($ZrO_2.Y_2O_3$) falls only slightly below. Even natural zircon ($ZrSiO_4$), with a high dispersion and an R.I. of nearly 2, can be difficult to distinguish from diamond if colourless. Despite such substitutes, ladies are unlikely to accept them as a 'girl's best friend'.

## 8.11  The chemical industry

The chemical industry depends largely on mineral products. One part of it is supplied with by-products from mineral fuels to form the coal-tar and petro-chemical industries which, in turn, provide us with solvents, alcohols, dyes, medical compounds, plastics, and man-made fibres. These are referred to in Chapter 7. Here emphasis is on inorganic minerals and chemicals.

### 8.11.1 Fertilizers

Modern agriculture is dependent on phosphate, nitrate and potash fertilizers. Lime is also important, usually supplied as crushed limestone. Phosphates were once supplied by recovering guano, the accumulated droppings of sea birds on islands off the Chilean coast, and from bone beds. Nowadays 85 per cent of phosphates are mined from pelletal sedimentary phosphorites resembling colitic limestones, the rest from bone beds of fish bones and shells replaced by phosphates, and from phosphatic muds. Mineral phosphate occurs in one of the several forms of apatite ($Ca_5(PO_4)_3(F,Cl,OH)$).

Phosphorites are processed with sulphuric acid to produce single, double or triple superphosphates of the general form $Ca(H_2PO_4)_2$. Thus the viability of a fertilizer industry frequently depends on a nearby source of sulphuric acid (section 8.11.3). Phosphates also play an important part in the detergent industry.

Nitrates were also first obtained largely from Chile, as caliche or Chile saltpetre evaporites (mixed nitrates, largely sodium nitrate), found in the Atacama desert. This source was unable to satisfy the demands of the explosives and other industries, let alone fertilizers, and nitrates are now produced from nitrogen fixed from the atmosphere.

### 8.11.2 Soda, potash, and lime

Some commodities are so useful it is best to look at them specifically. The salts of the alkali metals have a wide application in industry, especially those of sodium. Sodium chloride (NaC1, halite, rock salt) is perhaps the oldest industrial chemical; the Chinese drilled for it centuries before the Christian era, the Romans paid their legionnaires with it, giving us the word 'salary'. Much is extracted by evaporation of salt water in salt pans: some is pumped from underground, either as natural brine or by injecting water through boreholes and dissolving it out; some is mined underground from salt beds (Cheshire, UK, and Siberia, USSR), or from salt domes. Other salts are also recovered in these processes, including those of potash. Many naturally-occcuring salts go under unfamiliar commercial names. Sodium bicarbonate is called trona; natron or soda ash is sodium carbonate; sodium sulphate is soda cake or glauber salt. Potash does not appear to have attracted such colloquial names except, perhaps for alum $(KAl_3(SO_4)_2.(OH)_6)$ which occurs with acid to intermediate volcanic activity.

Lime or calcium minerals, apart from gypsum, are recovered from limestone in one of its many natural forms. Calcium carbonate has many applications in industry, including use as a cheap and generally available material for neutralizing acid effluents. It is also the basis of the numerous calcium salts and compounds. The uses of the alkali metal salts are so extensive, that it is impossible to cover them here; many are obvious.

### 8.11.3 Pyrite

*Pyrite* $(FeS_2)$ is commonly associated with sulphide metallic ores, usually occurring greatly in excess of the ore minerals themselves. Although pyrite is a sulphide of iron, it cannot be used as an iron ore because of its sulphur content. It is therefore essentially a gangue mineral which must be separated from the ore minerals before smelting and dumped as waste or tailings, where its oxidation by weathering often causes problems. As mentioned in Chapter 1 (section 1.2.1), pyrite may contain small amounts of cobalt, as in Africa, or sometimes gold, and so may sometimes technically be an ore of those metals. Unfortunately it is not always economically possible to extract them. Where there is need for sulphuric acid, pyrite again becomes a useful commodity; it may even be exported if conditions favour low-cost transport. The sulphide is roasted to sulphur dioxide $(SO_2)$ which is converted via the trioxide $(SO_3)$ to sulphuric acid. In many mining areas the smelting of sulphide ore minerals alone produces sufficient sulphur dioxide to satisfy the need for acid, so that again the pyrite gangue is dumped. Sulphuric acid is also produced from oil fields with carbonate reservoirs, for sulphur must be removed from the oil before refining. It may then come into direct competition with by-product sulphuric acid from smelters. Acid can also be made directly from elemental sulphur recovered from salt dome caps or other sulphur beds.

With new legislation looming, or already passed in many countries, regarding the discharge of sulphur dioxide into the atmosphere, many smelters will be producing sulphuric acid whether they like it or not. If they cannot sell the acid, they must neutralize it and, for copper smelters, that can add 30 per cent to production costs (Aitkin 1985).

### 8.11.4  The importance of chemicals

Many of the materials which are needed for a chemical industry are interdependent. For instance, the discovery of phosphates in eastern Turkey made it worthwhile to install a sulphuric acid plant at Ergani copper mine, some 100 km to the north, and to build a superphosphate plant in the same region. One mineral commodity in a country may not be worth exploiting on its own, and it is up to planners to visualize how it can be developed by searching for other mineral materials to combine it with. This requires geological appreciation of the surrounding area and, if nothing suitable appears likely, then the economics of importing materials must be considered. Geology is only too often ignored by planners who frequently seem to have little appreciation of non-metallic minerals, their sources, and the products made from them.

## 8.12  Conclusions

It has only been possible to give a few examples of the non-metallic use of minerals in industry here. Many more minerals are used than have been mentioned, many have several different applications. Gypsum was given as an example of multiple uses earlier. Another example is fluorite. Its use as a flux and in the manufacture of artificial cryolite has been described above, but fluorite is also used to manufacture glass and as an opacifier in ceramics. It is the basis of hydrofluoric acid too, and fluorine compounds go into insecticides and disinfectants, into non-stick materials used in industry and for domestic pots and pans, in freon gas for refrigeration plant and for propellants in aerosol cans. Fluorine products also fluoridize drinking water and up-grade uranium fuels by reducing the amount of non-radioactive isotope present. The mineral fluorite itself has long been valued in its purer forms as an ornamental stone under the name of blue john.

Not all industrial minerals are actually non-metallic. Some metallic compounds have uses in industry in addition to being sources of metals. Cadmium, chromium, mercury, and antimony pigments have already been described; zinc white is another pigment, and zinc oxide has been used as a pharmaceutical to aid healing since at least 300 BC, and is still with us. One zinc compound which faces us every day is the zinc sulphide 'phosphor' coatings on television screens, VDUs and other oscillographic apparatus.

Of all industrial minerals, perhaps quartz is the most outstanding. As sands and gravels, quartz is used as aggregate for concrete; as fine sand, it extends many building plasters and is an abrasive and scourer in numerous industrial operations. Quartz crystals control the frequency of oscillation in many electronic items, including clocks and radio transmitters; coloured quartz produces a wide range of semi-precious stones. Quartz-rich materials, in one form or another, are also used as fluxes in copper smelting and in refractory silica bricks. Quartz even produces chemicals, such as sodium silicate, or water glass, and of course, silicon itself. Finely ground, it is used in wear-resistant paints, such as those for painting the white lines on roads, and it is also, of course, the whole basis of the glass industry. Silica in other forms has many uses too; ground flint is added to ceramic clays, and diatomite, formed from the accumulated siliceous frustules of millions of marine organisms, is employed as a lightweight plaster aggregate, a filtrant, and as an absorbent for nitroglycerine. Several gemstones are composed of crypto-crystalline forms of silica.

Industry needs industrial minerals but unfortunately their importance is not always appreciated by those who plan our futures.

# CHAPTER 9

# Water, the essential mineral

Water has been described in various terms. In the 5th century BC, Pindar called it '. . . the best of all things'. Some call it Adam's wine; Buchan (1972) dubbed it the 'renewable mineral' because it is in constant circulation in the hydrologic cycle. Here, the term the essential mineral is preferred, for it emphasizes its importance, and any geologist who works in the Third World knows only too well how much time he spends looking for it. Even such apparently over-watered countries as Britain suffer occasional water shortages. Water is needed for domestic use; for drinking and cooking; for washing oneself, clothes and dishes; and for flushing lavatories. Every person in Britain needs about 150 litres of domestic water every day. Consumption in industry and farming is greater still.

Much of the water we use is from reservoirs formed by dams and, although the design of dams is greatly influenced by geology, such engineering geology is not covered in this book. Here we are interested only in the supply of underground water, and this aspect will be illustrated largely by examples from the lesser developed parts of the world where the need of water is most acute. In those regions it is usually the daily 'bread geologist' who has to find sources of water, rather than the hydrogeological specialist who solves the water problems of more developed countries.

## 9.1 The hydrologic cycle

The hydrologic cycle is the manner in which water from the sea, lakes, streams, rivers, and even moisture transpiring from the ground and plants, evaporates to be reprecipitated as rain, snow, or merely dew. Precipitation on land runs off in streams and rivers, and most eventually returns to the sea. Some, however, soaks into the ground, to seep downwards into the rocks as groundwater.

### 9.1.1 Water-tables and piezometric surfaces

The water-table represents the generalized theoretical upper surface of water-saturated rocks. Rocks above the water-table are not saturated, although they may still contain a considerable amount of moisture attached to mineral grains or, near the water-table, in capilliary openings (Fig. 9.1). Even soil contains some moisture. Rocks above the water-table are in the zone of aereation (vadose zone), because air is also present (cf. zone of oxidation, section 2.3). Rocks below the water-table are saturated with water, so no air is present; this is the zone of saturation (phreatic zone). This zone passes downwards to great depths and, as it gets deeper, so the groundwater becomes more brine-like. Some is water squeezed out of compacting rocks, some is meteoric (rain and surface) water from above. At very deep levels, only connate pore water occurs and, as it is in the unconnected pores of rocks, it cannot move. Deeper still, water is present only in chemical combination in minerals. For water supply purposes, we are concerned solely with the water which occurs within a few hundred metres of the surface.

The water-table is usually shown in diagrams as a continuous surface beneath ground level, reflecting the topography but lying deeper below hill tops than hill slopes, and emerging at ground level as streams, rivers, ponds and lakes (Fig. 9.2a). In effect, bodies of surface water represent the water-table where it has risen above ground level. The concept of a water-table is useful but limited. It implies that any well sunk to beneath the water-table will strike water. This is not so, for not all rocks are permeable and only permeable rocks can yield water. However, if a well is sunk through an impermeable stratum to permeable rocks beneath, water confined in those lower rocks will rise up the well to its rest level, that is, the level of the piezometric surface, a potential water-table related to the entry point of the confined water (Fig. 9.2c). Water-tables are not static. They fluctuate with the changing seasons, rising in wet weather, falling in dry. In very dry weather, a water-table may fall so low that it falls below river level and water from the river leaks down to the water-table (Fig. 9.2b). This happened in the Thames valley in two recent droughts, including that in 1984. Again, where wells draw water from the ground, the water-table becomes locally depressed (Fig. 9.2c) and if too much water is taken from too many wells, the whole water-table of a region may be lowered. This has happened in the London artesian basin. In Texas, farmers successfully sued for tax reductions on the grounds that the falling water-table had devalued their land (Flawn 1966).

In humid regions the water-table is usually closer to the surface than in arid lands, but not always. Water lies close to the surface in many parts of the Sahara and erosion, including wind erosion, has in places cut down to the water-table to form oases. On caravan routes in the Egyptian and Libyan deserts, the Romans quarried out underground cisterns in limestones to form water storage tanks at the water-table just beneath the surface. These *birs* were used by both the British and German armies during the 1939–45 war. Limestones have also been extensively tapped in Algeria to irrigate arid tracts, and Libya is in the early stage of doing the same on a huge scale. The water is largely 'fossil water' which has lain untapped for thousands of years. Is there sufficient to sustain such large irrigation projects; and will more water flow inwards from rocks outside the irrigated areas quickly

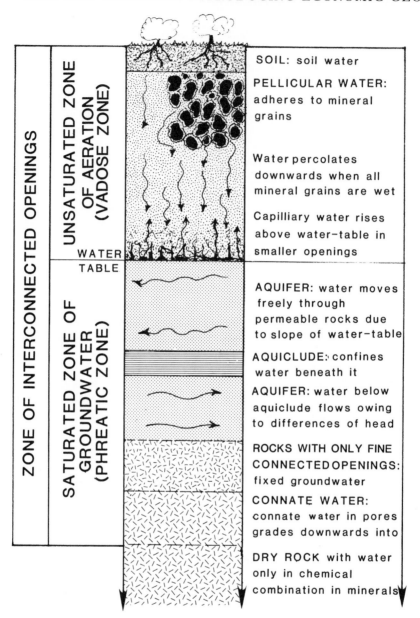

**Figure 9.1** The water content of rocks. Water moves downwards to maintain saturation in rocks beneath the water-table. Free water above the aquiclude will move down the slope of the water-table (Fig. 9.2); water confined below the aquiclude moves only by difference in head, as in a piped system. Permeability decreases with depth, reducing the ability of water to move. Connate water trapped in pores and sub-capillary openings does not normally move. Deeper still water is only present in combination with minerals, but even this can be released by metamorphic and other changes (see section 5.3.5).

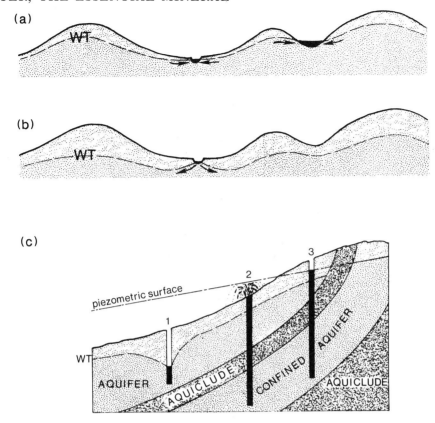

**Figure 9.2** (a) A normal water-table (WT). Its surface reflects topography in a subdued manner, emerging as streams and lakes where it intersects the surface. (b) If the water-table falls in a drought, river water may leak down to the water-table. (c) Positions of bored wells. Over-pumping at well 1 has drawn down the water-table and lowered the rest-level in the well. Well 2 has been sunk to a confined aquifer and, because the collar of the well is below the piezometric surface, water flows out freely at the collar; the well is artesian. Well 3 is not artesian because the well collar is above the piezometric surface; water will rise up the well only to its rest-level at the piezometric surface.

enough to recharge the rocks tapped, or will the water-table fall to an unacceptable level? Opinions differ. Only time will tell.

## 9.2  Aquifers and aquicludes

Aquifers are rocks which are water-permeable; aquicludes are those which are not. Aquifers may be granular rocks of many types, particularly those sandstones and conglomerates which are sufficciently uncemented to remain permeable. Water moves slowly between the granules. Quartzites can also be excellent water-bearing rocks provided they are well-jointed, for it is the joints which carry the water. Because quartzites have little soluble matter, their water is very pure. In southern Africa, Karroo dolerites are important aquifers because they too are well jointed, although their water is more likely to contain dissolved material. Limestones, with their solution-enlarged joints and beddings planes, make excellent aquifers too, but the water is hard from dissolved calcium. Even granites can carry considerable amounts of groundwater where, close to the surface, their joints are more open. Waters from igneous rocks, however, often precipitate fine iron-oxide sludge when left to stand; a few aquifers may contribute more harmful matter, including fine suspended mica and sericite. Some aquifers contaminate their waters with magnesium sulphate (Epsom salts), with less dangerous, but still unpleasant results!

Aquicludes are usually clay rocks or mica schists, with no granular porosity and little jointing. In East Africa, the weathered tops of granite and granite gneisses form effective aquicludes owing to the weathering of the feldspars to kaolinitic clays. Beneath this impermeable weathered capping lies a zone of open joints which carry water, and below that is almost unjointed dry rock. The clay-altered granite forms an effective seal to produce almost artesian conditions (Harris 1961, and see section 9.4).

### 9.3  Sources of groundwater

#### 9.3.1  Dug wells

Shallow, dug wells are a traditional source of water, and traces of them can be found even in the remains of ancient Jerusalem. Wells are by no means confined to arid areas. Many British farms once relied on them; some may still do, but such sources are no longer permissible for dairy purposes under Ministry of Agriculture regulations. The problem is that shallow wells are easily contaminated by nearby sewage and cess pits. Soil water from the aerated zone may percolate into poorly-lined wells too, especially during wet periods when the rise in water-table may flush impurities into the well from the aerated zone. Cholera and other afflictions can be spread by shallow wells. Despite their disadvantages, wells are cheap and easy to dig provided the water-table is not too deep. They need little more than a pick or shovel to sink, and villagers in the Third World are usually skilled at digging them and lining them with local materials. However, shallow wells may dry up in droughts as the water-table falls. Figure 9.3 shows a well in Anatolia used for watering sheep; the cable of the counterbalanced *shaduf* used for raising the water-filled bucket indicates the depth to water.

#### 9.3.2  Bored wells

Drilled wells, or boreholes, provide purer and more reliable sources of water. The bore is cased by iron pipe to prevent its walls collapsing and to exclude water from the aerated zone and the upper part of the saturated zone. Bores are usually sunk deeply into the aquifer to ensure a copious supply. Water which seeps into the bottom of the bore hole has been filtered by having percolated through a considerable distance of permeable rocks in the reducing environment of the saturated zone, thus lessening the chances of bacterial contamination. Unfortunately, pollution by mineral matter is sometimes a problem.

**Figure 9.3**
A *shaduf* for raising water from a well by counterbalancing the weight of the water-filled bucket, a traditional method used in the Middle East. The depth to water in this well is probably less than three metres.

Water boreholes are usually drilled by churn (percussion) drills which are cheaper to buy and cheaper to operate than rotary drills for holes of equal diameter (cf. section 6.4). Most water boreholes are only a few hundred metres deep, often much less than 200 m, with a diameter of 200 mm or more. Many are drilled through an impervious stratum to reach water confined in an aquifer beneath. Water then rises up the bore to reach its rest level at the piezometric surface. Conditions may even be artesian, with the rest-level above the ground surface; the water will then flow or even gush from the borehole without need of pumping (Fig. 9.2b). Usually, water must be pumped from the well either by hand-pump (Fig. 9.4) if the rest-level is relatively close to the surface, by wind-pump if deeper, or even by a motorized pump. Holes with wind or motorized pumps are furnished with a tank or cistern to store water and to provide a reserve for when the wind drops or the pump motor is not running. Many pumps restart automatically when the water level in the cistern drops below a certain level.

### 9.3.3 Qanats

*Qanat* is a Farsi (Persian) word to describe the undergrond canals which transfer water from its source to towns and villages up to seventy kilometres away in Iran; they are found in many other arid Asian regions under other names. The water source is usually in outwash fans in foothills which collect their water from winter snows; some water may even be fossil water. A shaft is dug up to 100 m deep at the water source and a 2 m by 2 m tunnel driven in the direction of the town to be supplied, and connected to a second shaft sunk fifty metres away. This second shaft is connected to a third, and that to a fourth, and so on until the destination is

**Figure 9.4** A hand pump in Busoga District, Uganda. Locally-made, easy to maintain and operate, such pumps are common in developing countries.

reached. The gradient of the unlined tunnel is such that water only just flows.

Water from a *qanat* is emitted into a surface channel at its exit and is then distributed through the village at a price, those drawing water closest to the exit paying more than those further away. Feeder *qanats* may flow into a main qanat to augment the supply, and many separate *qanats* may serve one town. From the air, the shafts look like long straight runs of evenly spaced bomb craters.

Blind white fish are reputed to live in the *qanats*, although in his book, *Blind white fish in Persia* (1966) Smith says the fish he found were neither blind nor white. He described *qanats* as the most efficient method devised by man to spread disease! Whatever else may be said of *qanat* systems, they do provide water in arid lands.

## 9.4  Searching for water

Many weird and wonderful ways have been used in the search for water in the past. Dowsers use divining rods and search for underground rivers. Underground rivers do exist in cavernous limestone regions but they are not what the dowsers refer to. Underground water is essentially in small openings and voids in aquifers and it moves very slowly. By following relatively simple geological rules, geologists in East Africa, even those newly recruited, were more successful at finding water than the professional dowsers who had once been employed. Water is often most difficult to find in areas of mica schists and phyllites where rocks are

(a)

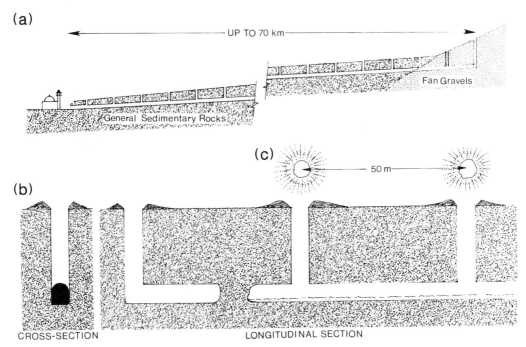

(b)

(c)

CROSS-SECTION        LONGITUDINAL SECTION

**Figure 9.5** Cross-sections of the *qanat* system of underground canals used in Iran and elsewhere in Asia. The top diagram shows the general course of a qanat from its water source in fan gravels to a town; side canals may feed the system. The lower diagram shows *qanat* construction, and an aerial view of two shafts.

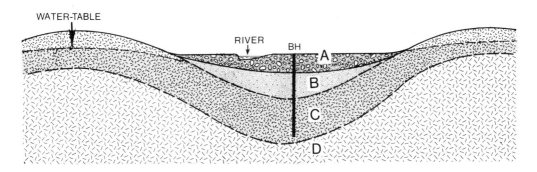

**Figure 9.6** Granite aquifers. Water is trapped in the jointed zone (C) above unaltered granite or gneiss (D) and confined by the overlying kaolinized granite (B); A is alluvial valley fill. Semi-artesian conditions result and water rises in the borehole (BH) to the piezometric surface, which is often only just below ground surface. The borehole is cased to ensure that percolating surface water in the alluvium does not contaminate the well water.

impervious and unjointed. In the tropics, in crystalline basement regions of apparently unending gneisses and granites, water can still be found. It occurs in what Jones (1985; and see Dixey, 1950) calls the sapropelic aquifer zone, between the unaltered rock below and the completely clay-altered material above. As Harris pointed out (1961), even sub-artesian conditions can exist, bringing water close to the surface (Fig. 9.6). The advice given to geologists in basement regions of Uganda in the 1950s was to site boreholes as far downslope and as far away from unweathered granitoid exposures as possible. Success rates were over 90 per cent.

The main principle in finding water is to know the geology of the area and its structure; to know what the aquifers are and where they occur. As always, a geological map helps. Where there are few exposures, difficulties do occur and geophysial aids may be called for; resistivity methods are probably the most useful. In general, finding water is seldom difficult; the problem is to find it exactly where it is wanted, at a convenient depth and in sufficient quantity to satisfy clients. Leopold (1974) gives a useful summary of the water problem.

It is seldom sufficiently appreciated by the layman that groundwater is a mineral material which occurs in rocks, and that a geologist is the person best equipped to find it. Too often, the geologist's opinion is asked too late.

# CHAPTER 10

# Mineral development: geology and geologists

Industry is dependent on products of the mineral industry, be they ores, non-metallics, or mineral fuels. Minerals must be found, and when found, mined. Geologists are essential to both the search for minerals and their exploitation and, even to a small extent, their processing.

Geologists associated with the mineral industries can be employed under three main heads: government organizations; mining, quarrying and oil companies; and teaching and research. Ideally, these groups should co-operate with each other; in practice, cooperation is seldom as close as is desirable.

## 10.1 Geology in government

The principal government organizations are the national geological surveys. In Britain, this is the British Geological Survey (BGS); in the United States, the United States Geological Survey (USGS); and in France the Bureau de Recherches Géologiques et Minières (BRGM). Other countries have similar organizations. Some countries have provincial surveys in addition to national departments, such as the state surveys of the USA administered by state universities. Local and district levels of government may also employ geologists, as do water authorities and conservancy councils in Britain.

### 10.1.1 National geological surveys

The prime task of a national geological survey is to provide regional geological maps to assist government planning, the development and maintenance of industries, and the discovery of areas worth prospecting for minerals. In the Third World, geological maps are often small-scale, lacking in detail, and may not even cover the whole country. Many surveys were established only in the last half century. Iran, for instance, had no geological survey until the 1950s; that in

Turkey was founded in 1936. The British survey is the oldest of all, but still dates to only 1835.

Not unnaturally, industrialized countries have geological maps at scales larger than less well developed countries. Britain is largely covered by geological maps at 1:50,000 and larger scales are available for coalfields and other geologically-important areas. The importance of geological maps cannot be over-emphasized, especially in undeveloped regions. Given a choice of moving into a country with geological maps or into one without, an exploration company would be naturally biassed towards the former, for its work would be made much easier.

The provision of geological maps is the primary task of a national geological survey. The maps may be used by many oganizations which have no connection with mining. Town planners, highway and railway developers, civil engineers and water authorities, even farmers at times, need to refer to geological maps. In addition to geological maps, geological survey departments may further refine the geological knowledge of their country with geophysical, geochemial, and other specialized maps. In Britain, government geophysical surveying has materially helped the discovery of offshore oil by commercial oil companies. Regional geochemical maps show the distribution of a wide range of metallic elements over a whole country. They are obviously useful to the mining industry, but they have other uses too; they monitor pollution, and can even indicate reasons for trace-element diseases in cattle. Geological survey departments provide many other services for the public, including information and advice, laboratory and ore dressing services, and access to type collections of fossils, rocks and minerals.

### 10.1.2 Government prospecting

The search for new mineral fields is part of the duty of a government geological survey but, in a free economy, prospecting for mineral ore bodies is considered to be the domain of the mining companies. In countries with planned economies, and in many Third World countries, governments are more closely engaged in basic prospecting, either because all mining is done by the state or, in the Third World, to attract outside capital. But, even in free economies, government departments may prospect during national emergencies, in time of shortage, or where there are special considerations. The British government, for instance, set up its own uranium prospecting organization in the 1940s in addition to encouraging prospecting by the public. Also, since nationalization of the coal industry in the later 1940s, all British coal prospecting is now done by British Coal, a state corporation.

In many countries, and by no means all associated with the Eastern Bloc, mining is done largely by state-owned mining companies which do their own prospecting or cooperate with state geological survey departments. In such countries, nearly all geologists, even those in the universities, are employed by the state, and are essentially civil servants.

### 10.1.3 Other national bodies

In Britain, county and district council planning departments often employ geologists to review housing and factory building applications, and to look at any other proposals which might affect the environment, including applications to quarry, drill, or mine. The British Nature Conservancy Council (NCC) employs geologists to watch over the environment too and also to ensure that sites of special scientific interest (SSSIs) are protected and preserved for geologists of later generations. Other countries have equivalent bodies.

### 10.1.4 Overseas interests

Many industrialized countries provide technical aid to less well developed countries. In Britain, the Overseas Development Administration (ODA) funds overseas geological aid through the Overseas Division of BGS. Aid may consist merely of provision of a specialist geologist or geophysicist for a specific project, or it may be a complete team. Similar work is done by the Office for International Geology of USGS funded through the Agency for International Development (AID). The French BRGM does overseas work too, some of it on a paid contractural basis. Many countries provide overseas geological aid, including most in Europe, China and Japan, and many in the Eastern Bloc.

The United Nations is another source of overseas aid. It supplies geological expertise by funding geologists through several of its branch organizations. It may establish a geological survey department, as in Iran: or it may finance large-scale projects, such as airborne geophysical surveys. It may even fund a university department. Generally speaking, overseas geological aid is directed towards encouraging the development of mineral resources, combined with training local geologists.

### 10.1.5 Geologists employed by geological surveys

Geologists employed by geological surveys cover many specialities. The backbone of any survey are the field geologists who do the regional geological mapping. In addition, the larger surveys employ photogeologists, geophysicists, geochemists, hydrogeologists, mining geologists, economic geologists and industrial minerals geologists. These people are supported by topographers, mineral economists, mining and drilling engineers, ore dressers, chemists, assayers and geochronologists. Smaller surveys in developing countries cannot afford such specialists and, in the very smallest surveys, it is the jack-of-all-trades field geologist, the infantryman of geology, who must try to cover as many aspects as possible. He probably leads the more interesting life!

## 10.2 Company geology

Companies concerned with searching for minerals, whether metallic, non-metallic, coal, oil or gas, are obviously prime employers of geologists. Geologists are also needed once a mineral has been found, although in a different capacity. There is usually a separation between the prospecting and mining divisions of a major company, not only because the techniques they use are different but so is their financing, and these two branches normally operate independently of each other.

### 10.2.1 Mining companies

Large mining companies fund prospecting separately from their mining activities, frequently under a different company name. Very large companies may, in any case, own many subsidiary mining companies, all operating independently in different countries. The prospecting company may therefore be only one of the many subsidiaries of a multinational holding company.

A prospecting company is essentially a geological department, run by geologists and mainly staffed by geologists. It employs many specialists, including ore geologists, geochemial prospectors, geophysicists, photogeologists and, these days, often geologists who can interpret satellite imagery. There will also be field geologists capable of making geological reconnaissance maps rapidly, and others who can make very detailed maps of small areas at very large scales. In the field, a prospecting party will probably work as a team from a central camp, supported, in remoter areas, by aircraft or helicopters. The emphasis is on speed to get things done.

Large prospecting companies are well equipped with laboratories at headquarters and can call on outside consultants for advice or services when needed. Drilling is usually farmed out to drilling companies, and some routine fieldwork and geochemistry may also be contracted for by one of the many independent technical services companies. Air photography, photogeology and airborne geophysics are also usually done by contract. Sub-contracting widens the scope of a prospecting company without the need for them to maintain specialist staff and expensive equipment which they cannot keep continuously employed.

Mining operations are more usually run by a mining engineer, although geologist mine managers are not unknown. The geology department of a mine, however, is a service department. It maps open pits and underground workings at very large scales (1:500 is normal) and up-dates the maps daily. It also has charge of sampling. The department is expected to advise management on where their ore is, its grade, tonnage, shape and composition, and how it may vary laterally and in depth. The mine geologists must provide a three-dimensional picture of the ore so that mining methods and workings can be planned well in advance. They must also solve any day-to-day problems caused by faulting and ensure optimum efficiency and production by seeing that the mining department can supply the mill continuously with a specific tonnage of ore at a pre-determined average grade. The geology department will also be expected to find adequate supplies of water suitable for the mill, machinery and domestic use, locate sources of neutralizers and fluxes for mill and smelters, and provide answers for any other geological and mineralogical difficulties that arise.

Coal is a specialist subject. Geologists who prospect for it are more sedimentologically and stratigraphically orientated than those looking for ores. A thorough knowledge of regional geology, stratigraphy and history is needed to discover concealed coalfields, but even during mining, coal seams are seldom as continuous or as flat as many people believe. Seams can be steeply inclined, folded and interrupted by numerous faults. What is astonishing is that the coal industry took so long to realize that geologists could help them.

### 10.2.2 Oil and gas industry

The search for oil and gas differs from prospecting for solid minerals in that oil-bearing structures are entirely sub-surface and there may be little apparent likelihood of hydrocarbons from surface indications. Exploration depends firstly on deciding where oil-bearing rocks are likely to occur. This is essentially a sedimentological problem linked to stratigraphy, with help from palaeontologists to determine the age of sequences. Structural geologists working with geophysicists then locate structures which could contain oil. Again, photogeologists and, increasingly, interpreters of satellite imagery, help in the primary search.

Once a structure has been located, geologists log cores brought to the surface by drilling and mud-loggers monitor progress of the hole. Mud-loggers use a wide range of computerized instruments to correlate geological formations; they measure rock porosity and test for hydrocarbons present, in addition to their original task of checking gas pressures and drilling mud needs. Once a reservoir has been located, reservoir engineers calculate reserves from the volume of the pay horizon, its porosiy and the levels of the gas/oil and oil/brine interfaces. They also determine yield and total recovery.

When oil production commences, the role of the geologist is virtually over except where he is needed to maintain reserves in the pools being exploited. Note, the description petroleum geologist is a catch-all term; he may be a sedimentologist, stratigrapher or palaeontologist (especially a micropalaeontologist), a structural geologist, reservoir engineer, geophysicist or a mud-logger. He may not even be a member of the oil industry at all, for he may be a consultant called in to answer a particular geological problem of stratigraphic, palaeontological or structural nature which has little to do with oil as such.

### 10.2.3 Technical service companies

A number of independent companies tender their geological services to industry. For instance, some specialize in airborne geophysics, others offer wider services. They contract for geological and photogeological surveys, geophysical work, geochemical prospecting, mineral studies and hydrogeological surveys anywhere in the world. Some offer only laboratory services, some small, almost one-man companies have specific expertise in a very special field. As in every other profession, geologists offer themselves as consultants on subjects in which they have wide experience. There is even the occasional geologist-cum-lawyer. Service companies and consultants are used by exploration and mining companies to supplement their own activities, either to supply extra staff during times of especial pressure, or to provide services for which they are not equipped. Subcontracting is common to all types of industry.

## 10.3  Academia

The third category of geological employment is in universities and polytechnics. If geologists are needed, they must be trained and many, but not all universities, have departments of geology. Research and development is also important in geology, as it is in the other applied sciences. Universities are the main, but not the only, centres of geological research.

### 10.3.1 Teaching

Here we are more concerned with the training of geologists for the mineral industries than in training geologists in general. Mineral industry geologists first need a good background in pure geology, but they should also graduate with at least some appreciation of the applied aspects of their science. This book indicates the wide range of subjects they can specialize in. Students cannot cover every branch of applied geology and tend to split naturally into groups of special interest. Some are more mineralogically inclined than others and so might also be more interested in mineral deposits than those who prefer fossils and stratigraphy. The latter students might suit the oil industry better. Those with a more mathematical mind may feel attracted to geophysics. Categorizing students into 'soft rock' and 'hard rock', however, has its dangers. Many ore deposits occur in soft rocks and have been formed from brines related to those which carry oil. Many industrial minerals are also soft rocks. Some universities provide courses in ore geology, industrial mineralogy and oil geology at undergraduate level; others hold intensive postgraduate courses in the same subjects. In general, British universities emphasize the economic aspects of geology to a far lesser extent than universities overseas, especially those in the Eastern Bloc who usually offer a four-year degree course against the British three-year system. Graduates must, however, always remember that a university is only their first step on the professional ladder; learning does not stop on graduation day. In the long run, it is professional experience which counts.

### 10.3.2 Research

Universities are centres of research in pure geology. They are often less well suited to undertake research in applied geology, unless specially equipped to do so. Much pure geological research is, however, of interest to the mineral industry. The discovery of plate tectonics, for instance, made the occurrence of many types of mineral deposit more understandable. Even techniques of more direct application have originated in universities, including many geophysical and geochemical prospecting methods. But universities are not the only places where applied geological research is done. The larger mining and oil companies have their own research departments. Consulting companies also research and develop methods and equipment, and several notable advances in geophysical prospecting have been made by them in recent years. But not all company research is applied. One mining company funded a research group on the premise that if only one discovery every ten years was useful to them, the cost was still worth their while. The same company even paid for publication and distribution of wholly fundamental research.

National geological survey departments undertake research too, although this is seldom properly recognized. Much of the work done by surveys is taken for granted and used by others with little credit given, yet similar work done in a university would be considered fundamental research and cause for acclaim. Universities are not the only places where discoveries are made.

Universities do, however, have staff with very special expertise in specific aspects of geology which are not available elsewhere. They can be, and are, consulted by industry when particular problems need to be solved. Such problems may merely concern the identification of fossils for an oil company or the identification of minerals for a mining company, or even a method of ore estimation for an awkward mine. Alternatively, industry may finance long-term university research into problems they have neither the time nor equipment to do themselves.

## 10.4  Conclusions

Geologists are widely employed in the minerals industry, far more so than fifty years ago when applied geologists were truly a rare breed. But not all geologists associated with ores, coal, oil and industrial minerals are directly employed by industry; some are members of geological surveys and not a few are members of universities. Unfortunately, the present (1986) recession has not been kind to the mineral industries; mining and prospecting have been heavily cut back and even some of the largest mines have closed. The oil industry has suffered too, although not as badly as metal mining. Coal, however, is an expanding industry worldwide, although not alas in Britain, where production has been steadily declining in the face of competing fuels. Probably, with the closure of many old and uneconomic British coal pits, production has now reached a temporary base level. Yet the future prospects of employment for geologists in the economic field should be good. The expanding world population needs more metals, industrial minerals and fuels, and sources must be found. It will be up to the geologist to find them and to help in their exploitation.

# References

Agricola, G. (1556). *De Re Metallica* (translated H.C. and L.H. Hoover, 1912), London, Mining Magazine.

Aitkin, K. (1985). Marketing concentrated smelter acid. *Eng. and Mining J.* 186 (5), 31–3.

Al Atia, M.J. and Barnes, J.W. (1975). Rubidium: a primary dispersion pathfinder at Ogofau Gold Mine, southern Wales, in *Geochemical exploration 1974*, (eds. I.L. Elliott and W.K. Fletcher), Amsterdam, Elsevier, 342–52.

Annels, A.E. (1979). Mufulira greywackes and their associated sulphides. *Trans. Inst. Min. Metall*, 88, B15–24.

Armbrust, G.A., Oyarzun, J. and Arias, J. (1977). Rubidium as a guide to ore in Chilean porphyry copper deposits. *Econ, Geol.* 72, 1086–1100.

Australian gemstones. (1979) *Min. Sc. and Engineering*, 11 (1) Jan.

Averitt, P. (1973). Coal, in *United States mineral resources*. (eds. D.A. Brobst and W.H. Pratt), U.S. Geol. Survey professional paper 820, Washington, U.S. Govt. Printing Office, 133–142.

Badham, J.P.N. (1981a). The origin of ore deposits in sedimentary rocks, in *Economic geology and geotectonics*, (ed. D.H. Tarling, London, Blackwell, 149–92.

Badham, J.P.N. (1981b). Shale-hosted Pb-Zn deposits — products of exhalation of formation waters. *Tran. Inst. Min. Metall.* 90, B70–6.

Bailey, E.H., Barnes, J.W. and Nackowski, M.P. (1978). Geology and ore deposits of the Kushk zinc-lead mine area, Iran. *Rept. 5th CENTO field training program in geol. mapping techniques*, Ankara, CENTO.

Barnes, J.W. (ed.) (1961). *The mineral resources of Uganda*. Bull. 4, Geol. Survey Uganda. Entebbe, Govt. Printer, 89 pp.

Barnes, J.W. and Bailey, E.H. (1972). Turkey's major mercury mine: how it was worked 8000 years ago. *World Mining* (European edition), 25(4), 49–55.

Bates, R.L. (1969). *Geology of the industrial rocks and minerals*. New York, Dover, 459 pp.

Beckman, H. (1976). *Geological prospecting of petroleum: geology of petroleum*, vol. 2, (transl. by Donald McLeod), London, Pitman, 183 pp.

Bender, F. (1982). Sufficient energy raw materials for everyone?, in *Resources for the 21st century*, (eds. F.C. Whitmore and M.E. Williams), Proc. Internat. Centenniel Symp. of U.S. Geol. Surv., Washington, 104–114.

Bethke, C.M. (1986). Hydrologic constraints on the genesis of the Upper Mississippi Valley mineral district from Illinois Basin brines. *Econ. Geol.* 81(2), 223–49.

Bignell, R.D. (1975). Timing, distribution and origin of submarine mineralization. *Trans. Inst. Min. Metall.* 84, B1–6.

Bloxam, T.W. and Owen, T.R. (1985). Anthracitization of coals in the South Wales coalfield. *International J. of Coal Geol.* **4**, 299–307.

Boyle, R.W. (1968). *The geochemistry of silver and its deposits*. Geol. Surv. Canada, Bull. 160. Ottawa, Dept. Energy, Mines and Resources.

(1979). *The geochemistry of gold and its deposits*. Geol. Surv. Canada, Bull. 280. Ottawa, Dept. Energy, Mines and Resources.

Brinkman, R. (1976). *Geology of Turkey*. Amsterdam, Elsevier.

Brookins, D.G. (1981). *Earth resources, energy and the environment*. Columbus, Ohio, Charles Merrill.

Brooks, R.R. (1983). *Biological methods of prospecting for minerals*. New York, Wiley.

Brown, A.C. (1978). Stratiform copper deposits — evidence for their post sedimentary origin. *Minerals Science and Engineering* **10**, 172–81.

Brown, G.C. and Skipsey, E. (1986). *Energy Resources*. Milton Keynes, Open University Press.

Buchan, S. (1972). The renewable mineral — challenge to the geologist, in *Mineral exploitation and economic geology*. University of Wales Inter-collegiate colloquium, Gregynog. 7–13.

Burger, J.R. (1985). Cerrejon: coal from Columbia. *Eng. and Min. J.*, **186**(4), 32J–32N.

Callahan, W.H. (1964). Palaeophysiographic premises for prospecting for strata bound base metal mineral deposits in carbonate rocks, in *CENTO symposium on base metals and mining geology*, Ankara, 191–248.

(1967). Some spatial and temporal aspects of the localization of Mississippi Valley-Appalachian type ore deposits, in *Genesis of stratiform lead-zinc-barite-fluorite deposits*, Lancaster, Penn., Econ. Geol. Publishing Co., 14–19.

Campbell, I.H., McDougall, T.J. and Turner, J.S. (1984). *Econ. Geol.* **79**, 1905–13.

Cann, J.R. (1981). Ore deposits of the ocean crust, in *Economic geology and geotectonics*, (ed. D.H. Tarling), London, Blackwell Scientific Publications, 119–134.

Chase, R.L., Delaney, J.R., Karsten, J.L., Johnson, H.P., Juniper, S.K., Lupton, J.E., Scott, S.D., Tunnicliffe, V., Hammond, S.R. and McDuff, R.E. (1985). Hydrothermal vents on an axis seamount of the Juan de Fuca ridge. *Nature* **133**, 212–4.

Colley, H. (1976). Classification and exploration guide for Kuroko-type deposits based on occurrences in Fiji. *Trans. Inst. Min. Metall.* **85**, B190–200.

Constantinou, G. and Govett, G.J.S. (1972). Genesis of sulphide deposits, ochre and umber of Cyprus. *Trans. Inst. Min. Metall.* **81**(783), B34–46.

Dahanayake, K. and Krumbein, W.E. (1986). Microbial structures in oolitic iron formations. *Mineral. Deposita* **21**, 85–94.

Dawson, J.B. (1971). Advances in kimberlite geology. *Earth Sci. Rev.* **7**, 187–214.

Dietrich, R.V. and Skinner, B.J. (1979). *Rocks and rock minerals*. New York, John Wiley and Sons, 319 pp.

Dietz, R.S. (1964). Sudbury structure as an astrobleme. *J. Geology*, **72**(4), 412–434.

Dixey, F. (1950). *A practical handbook of water supply*. London, Murby, 573 pp.

Edwards, I.E.S. (1947). *The pyramids of Egypt*. London, Pelican, 319 pp.

Edwards, R. and Atkinson, K. (1986). *Ore deposit geology*. London, Chapman and Hall, 466 pp.

Esder, T. and Simsek, S. (1977). The relationship between the temperature-gradient, distribution and geological structure in the Izmir-Seferihisar geothermal area, Turkey, in *Symposium on geothermal energy*. Ankara, CENTO, 93–115.

Evans, A.M. (1980). *An introduction to ore geology*. Edinburgh, Blackwell Scientific Publications.

Flawn, P.T. (1966). *Mineral resources*. Chicago, Rand McNally, 406 pp.

Foley, G. (1976). *The energy question*. London, Pelican, 244 pp.

Ford, T.D. and King, R.J. (1965). Layered epigenetic galena-barite deposits in the Golconda mine, Brassington, Derbyshire. *Econ. Geol.* **60**, 1686–701.

Frietsch, R. (1978). On the magmatic origin of iron ores of the Kiruna type. *Econ. Geol.* **73**, 478–85.

Glennie, K.W. (1984). *Introduction to the petroleum geology of the North Sea.* London, Blackwell, 236 pp.

Goldfarb, M.S., Converse, D.R., Holland, H.D. and Edmond, J.H. (1983). The genesis of hot spring deposits on the East Pacific Rise, 21°N. *Econ. Geol. Monograph*, 5, 184–97.

Gomez, B. (1985). Saxonvale mine. *Eng. and Mining J.*, 186(5), 16J–160.

Guilbert, J.M. and Parks C.F. Jr. (1986). *The geology of ore deposits.* New York, Freeman, 985 pp.

Harben, P.W. and Bates, R.L. (1984). *Geology of the non-metallics.* New York, Metall. Bulletin Inc., 393 pp.

Harris, N.H. (1961). Water, in *Mineral resources of Uganda* (ed. J.W. Barnes). Bull 4, Geol. Surv. Uganda, 48–53.

Haynes, D.W. (1986a). Stratiform copper deposits hosted by low-energy sediments: I. Timing of sulphide precipitation — an hypothesis. *Econ. Geol.*, 81(2), 250–64.

   (1986b). Stratiform copper deposits hosted by low-energy sediments: II. Nature of source rocks and composition of metal-transporting water. *Econ. Geol.*, 81(2), 266–80.

Hekinian, R., and Fouquet, Y. (1985). Volcanism and metallogenesis of axial and non-axial structures on the East Pacific Rise near 13°N. *Econ. Geol.* **80**(2), 221–49.

Hutchison, C. S. (1983). *Economic deposits and their tectonic setting.* London, Macmillan, 365 pp.

Jacobsen, J.B.E. (1975). Copper deposits in time and space. *Minerals Science and Engineering* **7**(4), 337–71.

Jensen, M.L. and Bateman, A.M. (1979) *Economic mineral deposits.* New York, John Wiley and sons, 593 pp.

Johnson, G.A.L. (1981). Coal in *Economic geology and geotectonics*, (ed. D.H. Tarling), London, Blackwell, 99–118.

Jones, M.J. (1985). The weathered zone acquifers of the basement complex areas of Africa. *Q.J. of Eng. Geol.*, 35–46.

Jowett, E.C. (1986). Genesis of Kupferschiefer Cu-Ag deposits by convective flow of Rotliegende brines during Triassic rifting. *Econ. Geol.* 81(8), 1823–37.

King, B.C. (1949). *The Napak area of southern Karamoja, Uganda.* Geol. Surv. Uganda Mem. 5. Entebbe, Govt. Printer. 57 pp.

Knill, J.L. (1978). *Industrial geology.* Oxford, Oxford University Press.

Leopold, L.B. (1974). *Water — a primer.* San Francisco, Freeman and Co., 172 pp.

Love, D. (1985). Syncrude's earthmoving panorama. *Engineering and Mining Journal*, 186(7), New York, McGraw-Hill, 26–30.

Lowell, J.D. and Guilbert, J.M. (1970). Lateral and vertical alteration mineralization zoning in porphyry or deposits. *Econ. Geol.* **65**, 373–408.

McKinstry, H.E. (1948). *Mining geology.* New York, Prentice-Hall, 680 pp.

Mero, J.L. (1965). *The mineral resources of the sea.* Amsterdam, Elsevier, 312 pp.

Mitchell, A.H.G. and Garson, M.S. (1976). Mineralization at plate boundaries. *Min. Sci. and Eng.* 8(2).

Moffat, A. (1986). The world's deepest borehole. *Geodrilling*, No. 40, 17–18.

Owen, T.R. (1973). *Geology in South Wales explained.* Newton Abbott, David and Charles, 211 pp.

Pain, S. (1986). Hot spots in the Atlantic Ocean. *New Scientist*, 111(1520), p. 29.

Parak, T. (1975). Kiruna iron ores are not 'intrusive-magmatic ores of Kiruna type'. *Econ. Geol.* **70**, 1242–58.

Park, C.F. and McDiarmid, R. (1964). *Ore deposits*. San Francisco, Freeman and Co., 475 pp.

Pattison, E.F. (1979). The Sudbury sublayer. *Can. Mineral.* **17**, 257–74.

Phillips, W.J. (1972). Hydraulic fracturing and mineralization. *J. Geol. Soc. Lond.* **128**, 337–59.

(1986). Hydraulic fracturing effects in the formation of mineral deposits. *Trans. Inst. Min. Metall* **95**, B17–25.

Pitman, F. (1981). Brazil programs a 25,000 bbl/day unit for '85 and a twin for '88. *Engineering and Mining Journal*, **182**(6), McGraw-Hill, 100–5, 106–9.

Plant, J.A. and Slater, D. (1986). Regional geochemistry — potential developments. *Trans. Inst. Min. Metall.* **95**,B63–69.

Pretorius, D.A. (1975). The depositional environment of the Witwatersrand goldfields: a chronological review of speculations and observations. *Minerals Science and Engineering*, 7(1), 18–47.

Rose, A.W., Hawkes, H.E. and Webb, J.S. (1979). *Geochemistry in mineral exploration*, 2nd ed. London, Academic Press, 657 pp.

Russell, M.J. (1975). Lithogeochemical environment of the Tynagh base-metal deposit, Ireland, and its bearing on ore deposition. *Trans. Inst. Min. Metall.* **84**, B128–33.

Sarp, B. (1961). Zonguldak bituminous coalfield. *Symposium on coal*. Ankara, CENTO, 151–8.

Sato, T. (1977). Kuroko deposits: their geology, geochemistry and origin, in *Volcanic processes and ore genesis*. Inst. Min. Met, /Geol. Soc. London, 153–161.

Selley, R.C. (1985) *Elements of petrolium geology*, New York, Freeman, 449 pp.

Sillitoe, R.H. (1973). The tops and bottoms of porphyry copper deposits. *Econ. Geol.* **67**, 184–97.

Skinner, B.J. (1976) *Earth resources*. London, Prentice-Hall, 152 pp.

Skirrow, R. and Coleman, M.L. (1982). Origin of sulphur and geothermometry of hydrothermal sulphides from the Galapagos Rift, 86°W. *Nature*, **299**, 142–4.

Smith, A. (1966). *Blind white fish in Persia*. London, Unwin, 207 pp.

Stanton, R.L. (1978). Mineralization in island arcs with particular reference to the south-west Pacific region. *Proc. Australas. Inst. Min. Metall.* **268**, 9–19.

Tarling, D.H. (ed.) (1981). *Economic geology and geotectonics*. London, Blackwell.

Trotter, F.M. (1948). Devolatilization of coal seams in South Wales. *Q.J. Geol. Soc.* **104**, 387–437.

Watson, J. (1983). *Geology and man*. London, Allen & Unwin, 150 pp.

White, L. (1985). India sets its sights on coal self-sufficiency within 15 years. *Engineering and Mining Journal*, McGraw-Hill.

(1986). Polish copper. *Engineering and Mining Journal*, **187**(2), 26–30.

Whitmore, F.C. Jr., Williams, M.E. (eds.) (1979). *Resources for the 21st century*. Proc. Int. Centennial Symp. of U.S.G.S. Prof. paper 1193. Washington, U.S. Govt. printing Off., 345 pp.

Wolfe, J.A. (1984), *Mineral resources: a world review*.London, Chapman and Hall, 293 pp.

*World Mining Equipment* (ed. Suttill, K.R.) (1986). Clinton, Iowa, U.S.A., 10(3), p. 13.

Wright, J.B. (ed.) (1973). *The earth's physical resources — 2. Energy resources*. Open University, 2nd level science course S26 — block 2. Milton Keynes, Open Univ. Press.

Wyllie, P.J. (1979) Kimberlite magmas from the system peridotite-$CO_2$-$H_2O$, in *Kimberlites, diatremes and diamonds: their geology, petrology and geochemistry*. Proc. 2nd Internat. Kimberlite Conference (eds. F.R. Boyd and H.O.A. Meyer). Washington, American Geophys. Union.

# Index